Nurture *for* the Nurturer

May you be abundantly
Nurtured —
Coach Larita Taylor

(Cousin Ann Wells-Webb's step daughter)

Nurture *for* the Nurturer

A 12 Day Meditational and Technical Guide for Breastfeeding Mothers

Larita Taylor, PHD, MPH, CLC

Illustration by Larita Taylor

Twenty One Sixty Publishing

Memphis, TN

To request permissions, contact the author at larita@webbmarkhealth.com.

ISBN 978-1-7342042-3-0 (Paperback)
Library of Congress Control Number: 2021940997

Edited by Danica J. Bora
Cover Art by Larita Taylor
Layout by Delano Taylor

First Paper Back Edition July 2021

Twenty One Sixty Publishing, LLC
4728 Spottswood Ave, PMB 273
Memphis, TN 38117-4817
www.twentyonesixty.com

Printed in the United States of America.

To my dearest daughter, who will be the most important recipient of the knowledge gathered in this book, and all the women who were robbed of their opportunity to nurture their own children in this way, may you experience the deepest joys and triumphs of nurturing your own soul as you nurture others.

Acknowledgements

Thank you to my biggest cheerleaders, my children, who provided the stories for the book, and my husband for your constant nurturing throughout the writing process and art renditions. You three are my greatest treasures. Dr. Marian Levy you are the best mentor ever! Dr. Julie Ware, Jamila, Tiana and the BSTARS thank you for helping me to venture into the wonderful world of breastfeeding. Lisa, Danica, Kimathi, Kimary, Sjhira, and Dell you have served as literary midwives throughout this process. Without your eyes and hands this work would not be what it is today. Mommy you nurtured me and Daddy you coached me into my destiny. I am eternally grateful for you both. Finally, El Shaddai, I'll forever be fully devoted to you because you have drawn me from the turbulent waters of life.

Table of Contents

Introduction

Congratulations for considering breastfeeding! If you have made it through one day, you have already made a significant contribution to your baby's health. Or maybe you have not yet delivered your baby, but you are curious about the endeavor to breastfeed. Whether you have already started breastfeeding, are still expecting, or maybe just reading to better support someone else, this book is designed to be a companion for a new mother adventuring into the first couple of weeks of breastfeeding and beyond. While anyone can benefit from the content, I believe the best use of this guide would be by a mother during the early days of breastfeeding. **It is not meant to be read in one sitting, but rather one day at a time.** Consider it on the job training.

Why twelve days? The first days and weeks of breastfeeding are foundational to having a healthy and rewarding breastfeeding journey. The first two weeks after birth are the most critical period for a mother to establish her milk supply. Not that it cannot be done at any other time, but my own research [1] and that of others shows that many well-intended mothers quit breastfeeding by the first or second week if their challenges are not addressed. A mother's early return to work coupled with her need to establish a consistent feeding routine for her newborn prior to returning to work, may be one of the reasons many mothers in the USA give breastfeeding a short trial period.

---

[1] Ware, Julie L., Larita Webb, and Marian Levy. "Barriers to breastfeeding in the African American population of Shelby County, Tennessee." Breastfeeding Medicine 9.8 (2014): 385-392.

Although more women have entered occupations outside the home than ever before and despite evidence that increased access to paid maternity leave increases the start and continuation of breastfeeding, unfortunately only 16% of all mothers in the USA have access to paid leave through their employer and 23% of all mothers in the USA return to work after 10 days because of the lack of paid leave. I chose 12 days because most women will have at least 10-14 days of uninterrupted contact with their infant, and 12 falls in the middle.

Also, I am aware of special circumstances like the hospitalization of a mother or a baby, or a mother being in a detention facility or incarcerated, which may cause the mother to be separated from her newborn(s) earlier than 10-14 days. Mothers in these circumstances may need extra encouragement to continue to breastfeed despite the barriers. I hope this book will be one of those resources.

While this book provides a limited amount of technical information about breastfeeding, it is not intended to be a comprehensive manual about how to breastfeed. There are many great books for that. While I was breastfeeding, I longed for a devotional/meditational book that specifically addressed my circumstance as a breastfeeding mother because of how much time I spent in that position, but I did not find one. I found myself in need of motivation to stay on my journey. So, I searched the Bible to see if there were any references or encouragement about breastfeeding. I was surprised at the number of references I found, and the motivation these scriptures provided me. As I encountered challenges with breastfeeding, I also found a new understanding of God's parental perspective in our struggle to grow and develop. I could see parallels between my attempts to breastfeed my babies and God's attempt to nurture and sustain humanity. Ironically, I could see the similarities between my newborns' behavior when they are hungry and how I behave when I have unmet needs. This book is a compilation of the biblical insights I gained.

Each day is designed to nourish you as a mother, like a meal would nourish your body. The sections are broken down like a full meal: an appetizer, an entrée, a refreshment (drink), and occasionally dessert. The appetizer consists of emotionally stimulating anecdotes that serve to wet your palate for the heartier entrée composed of technical facts and evidence-based research about breastfeeding. The entrée is followed by a refreshment in the form of a spiritual meditation that compares the mechanics of breastfeeding to practical skills for soul care. You may go in order, as the topics are labeled by days, or you can skip around. I do encourage you to read all the entries, as you most likely will encounter each aspect as you continue to breastfeed.

As the cover illustration depicts, I envisioned that a mother would read or listen to this meditational and technical guide, while feeding her infant at the breast. However, many of the concepts are still applicable if you pump your breastmilk or use your hand to get the milk from your breast, which is properly called manual expression. I wrote the refreshment sections keeping in mind mothers reading this book while pumping or manually expressing their breastmilk. It may be one of the few times where you are alone and undisturbed! Additionally, an appendix is included to provide a quick overview of the laws in each of the U.S. states and territories that support a mother's ability to breastfeed almost anywhere, a policy statement to help guide the implementation of breastfeeding policies in some jails and prisons, and a list of breastfeeding advocacy and support organizations. Just pack this book with your pump as a quick reference and motivational guide if you return to work or to any facility that temporarily separates you from your baby.

Finally, I began writing this book in the beginning of January 2020, before the world was consumed with the Coronavirus pandemic, and the lessons about nurturing yourself are more relevant now than ever. While the Coronavirus pandemic ushered in many devastating changes, more employers than ever before began offering their employees the option to work from home. If the trend is sustained, the option to work from home could be a blessing in disguise for working mothers just starting their breastfeeding journey. In case you are wondering, leading health organizations still consider breastfeeding a best practice even during the Coronavirus pandemic. Ultimately, no matter your situation, I pray that as you read this book you will experience the mothering heart of God and better understand God's compassion and care for you as you care for your new baby or babies. Bon Appétit! Enjoy and nurse on momma, nurse on!

Coach Taylor

The Menu

$\mathcal{D}ay$ 1

Overcoming Social and Cultural Resistance to Breastfeeding

"Even jackals offer the breast; they nurse their young, but the daughter of my people has become cruel, like the ostriches in the wilderness. The tongue of the nursing infant sticks to the roof of its mouth for thirst; the children beg for food, but no one gives to them."-Lamentations 4:3-4.

Appetizer

In no way is this scripture meant to shame anyone for considering an alternative feeding method to breastfeeding for their baby. I was not breastfed, and I never saw anyone do it growing up, except in a movie about a 5-year-old boy emperor in China who was breastfed by his mother. Needless to say, this first presentation of breastfeeding appeared foreign to me. While I dreamed about having children, I never considered breastfeeding them. This was not because I was repulsed by breastfeeding or rebelling against nature. No one had ever presented it to me as an option for infant feeding until I was taking a nutrition course in my Master of Public Health program.

Equipped with the facts, I knew I would breastfeed my children whenever I was blessed to have them, but also, I knew I would be going against the cultural norm in my community where breastfeeding was no longer the norm. In the African American community women had a long history of breastfeeding their children like everyone else before the invention of formula. However, during slavery, many women had been forced to serve as wet nurses to their slave master's children, which caused some to associate breastfeeding with the forcible subjugation of their bodies and a period of trauma.[2] In this case, formula feeding could be seen by some as a symbol of liberation and an opportunity to delineate their future

---

[2] West, E., & Knight, R. J. (2017). Mothers' milk: Slavery, wet-nursing, and black and white women in the antebellum south. Journal of Southern History, 83(1), 37-68.

from the painful past. That thought is much like the women's liberation movement, in general.

Others were just bombarded by formula companies who suggested that formula was better or a symbol of affluence, especially since more affluent women have had a history of outsourcing infant feeding to others. That is why wet nurses, women who breastfeed other people's children, were in such high demand before, during, and after slavery in the USA and around the world. In the USA, not only were slaves used as wet nurses, but poorer women from all ethnic backgrounds used wet nursing as a source of income.[3] In Brazil, enslaved African wet nurses were such a commodity that politicians passed a law to free slave children so that their mothers would be free from the responsibility to their own children and be available to nurse their slave master's children with no competition for their breastmilk supply.

Whether you are from a culture like mine or not, I want to equip you with some facts and hopefully fresh perspectives to help reinforce your decision to breastfeed. If you happen to be from a minority group or oppressed group, breastfeeding can be a form of reclamation and restitution. Take your body back and use it for the benefit of your own family.

In my research with about 100 focus group participants in a community with low breastfeeding rates, people were just uneducated about breastfeeding and allowed taboo and folklore to replace truth. Several participants either heard other people say or

---

[3] Golden, J. (2001). A social history of wet nursing in America: From breast to bottle. Ohio State University Press.

personally believed things like "it's nasty for a woman to breastfeed" or "it's just not right." [4]The women in my research study were not alone in their thinking. Some of their ideas were present in the American medical establishment as well. Once during a breastfeeding seminar, the presenter, who was a passionate breastfeeding advocate, recounted a story about the resistance she received from medical doctors when she was educating a group of physicians on the need to promote breastfeeding a child for a year or more. One male medical doctor disagreed with the presenter's recommendation by asking "how long must man be a suckling?" The presenter replied, "My husband still gets milk with his cookies." It was a mic drop moment. To the presenter's point, if a grown man can still latch on, surely the infant who needs his or her mother's milk for nutritional purposes can still latch on.

Similarly, some women in my research study mentioned not wanting their breast to appear distorted because of breastfeeding which they believed would be "a turn off" to their romantic partner. In some cultures where there is a high premium on beauty and perky breasts, both affluent and poorer women sometimes choose to forego breastfeeding for fear of how it may impact their romantic and/or economic opportunities. In societies where women are marginalized, sexuality or being viewed as sexy is one of the few ways for women to gain affirmation, money, and power. This trend does not just impact super models or sex workers,

---

[4] Ware, Julie L., Larita Webb, and Marian Levy. "Barriers to breastfeeding in the African American population of Shelby County, Tennessee." Breastfeeding Medicine 9.8 (2014): 385-392.

but almost any industry. Though I can understand the pressure to conform to societal norms of beauty when it is perceived that your appearance will impact your economic gain, I do believe the pressure can be overcome if we focus on the bigger picture – the lifelong health of our baby.

Other people have resisted breastfeeding because it has become a socioeconomic status symbol. For example, in some areas of the USA, breastfeeding seems to be a privilege of the affluent, with poorer mothers inundated with formula advertising, free formula from government sponsored programs, and less accommodating working conditions that make breastfeeding seem out of reach. In other communities, breastfeeding is associated with poverty and the inability to access clean drinking water or afford formula.

Other people associate breastfeeding with being part of the natural parenting revolution, which is stereotyped as shunning any manmade interventions like hospital assisted births, exchange vaccinations for chicken pox parties, eat sugarless foods and other less popular ideas. While nothing is wrong with any of these choices, our society has fallen victim to the concept of groupthink, which is fascinated with labeling people and "all or nothing" kind of thinking. So, if people subscribe to any one of the previously mentioned beliefs, people assume that you believe in all the thoughts associated with the label. People who don't like being categorized, like myself, may inadvertently shun breastfeeding for fear of being labeled. This is a needless and useless burden for any mother to bear.

So much baggage has been associated with breastfeeding. In any case, a woman's decision to breastfeed or not to breastfeed has been interpreted to mean more than what it is, which is a way for a mother to feed her baby.

Entrée

Today's scripture highlights the use of the breast to feed or "nurse" the young as the preferred plan and design of God. Because of our hypersexualized society, many people associate women's breasts with sex acts, to put it simply, and either have forgotten or disregard one of the original functions of breasts. This is evident in the number of state laws that had to be passed to declare that public breastfeeding should not be treated as a lewd act or violation of public nudity laws.

While breasts can play a role in erotic arousal, I believe God's original purpose for them to sustain life remains. The purpose and design of breasts and/or nipples is evident throughout all of nature. Cows have teats for their calves to nurse. Cats nurse their kittens. Dogs nurse their puppies, and even jackals, the wildest of animals, nurse their young. This design was a recession-proof and famine-proof way to guarantee that babies would always have something to eat. Breastfeeding is nature's way and its FREE! Would it not be odd to see a cat nursing a dog or a dog nursing a cow? Even more so, would you allow a human infant to latch on to the nipple of a cow or a goat? Now that is not natural, but in essence, that is what our society often promotes as the norm by shaming breastfeeding mothers and heavily promoting formula made from cow's milk.

Formula has its place because sometimes it is necessary. There are only a few medical reasons that would require the use of supplemental formula. For instance, infants born with galactosemia, or phenylketonuria have deficiencies preventing them from properly breaking down certain components in breastmilk. Also, birth defects that make it challenging for an infant to latch, the mother having a disease that may pass through her breastmilk, or the mother having an inadequate supply of breastmilk and human donor milk is not available are reasons to use formula. In case you are wondering, having Covid-19 does not require a mother to use formula.

Currently, even mothers who have contracted COVID-19 are encouraged to breastfeed if they practice safe hygiene measures, which may include pumping or hand expressing her breastmilk into a bottle while wearing a face mask. This decision is based on limited data where researchers have sampled breastmilk of COVID-19 mothers and have not found the virus present in the milk except in a few cases. When COVID-19 was found in the breastmilk, the milk may have become contaminated because the mother did not wear a face mask while she was pumping or expressing her milk. More importantly, researchers have discovered that COVID-19 antibodies pass through breastmilk. Based on these findings, leading health organizations including WHO (World Health Organization) and American Academy of Pediatricians still recommend breastfeeding among these mothers. Yet that may change as more data is collected.

You may hear naysayers regarding breastfeeding, but just drown out the noise with truth. While there are limited reasons why an infant would need formula, there are dozens of reasons why an infant needs your breastmilk. Nature has said it. God has said it, and now let me say it in French to make it sound more sophisticated. Breastfeeding truly is AU NATURALE.

Refreshment

Where do you go to get your nourishment? Do you see God the creator as a nurturer? While many people from Jewish or Christian traditions reference God as Father, many have missed the references to the mothering nature of God. Afterall, in the very beginning in Genesis, the Bible says that both male and female reflect the image of God. "So, God created mankind in his own image, in the image of God he created them; male *and female* he created them." – Genesis 1:27 (NIV). Even at the end of Jesus' life right before going to Calvary he uses maternal language to describe his desire to rescue and deliver the children of Israel.

"Jerusalem, Jerusalem, you who kill the prophets and stone those sent to you, how often I have longed to gather your children together, *as a hen gathers her chicks under her* wings, and you were not willing." - Matthew 23:37 (NIV).

Furthermore, one of the first revelations of the character of God to the children of Israel is the term EL Shaddai, which some Hebrew scholars translate as "the breasted one" because it comes from the Hebrew word for breast. Yet it is most often translated as God

Almighty alluding to all sufficiency. Just as your milk is designed to be all sufficient in providing your baby's nutritional needs for the first 6 months of life, God, or El Shaddai, is equipped to nurture and sustain you for your entire life by promising to deliver, protect, and comfort you.

As today's passage highlights, it is natural for the creature to turn to its creator for nourishment. Have you tried asking other people or sought other ways to fulfill you only to discover your tongue sticking to the roof of your mouth because those sources have left you thirsty? Do you find yourself feeling as though you must beg and plead for your basic needs, such as food, shelter, clothes, security, or affirmation? Have you considered that maybe you are expecting the wrong source to fulfill those needs? Consider turning to your Creator, God, to quench your thirst. El Shaddai, the many breasted one, has an abundant supply. The Bible promises in Philippians 4:19 "my God will meet all your needs according to the riches of his glory in Christ Jesus."

Day 2

Goal Setting and Planning for Breastfeeding Success

"For you created my inmost being you knit me together in my mother's womb. I praise you because I am fearfully and wonderfully made; your works are wonderful; I know that full well. My frame was not hidden from you when I was made in the secret place, when I was woven together in the depths of the earth. Your eyes saw my unformed body; all the days ordained for me were written in your book before one of them came to be." -Psalm 139:13-16

"Yet you brought me out of the womb; you made me trust in you, even at my mother's breast."- Psalm 22:9.

Appetizer

No matter what your current circumstances are as you start this journey, whether at home, at work, in a hospital or birthing center, in a detention facility, incarcerated, or in any other facility, God knew exactly where you would be at this point in your life. I believe in God's providence, and he knew you would need encouragement, so he allowed me to be your cheerleader. As a professional public health researcher, breastfeeding advocate and, more importantly, a mother of two breastfed children, 16 months for the first child and 26 months for the second, I have learned that having a clearly defined goal, commitment and support are the three most important factors in meeting your breastfeeding goal. This passage of scripture highlights the fact that God has goals and plans for everything He created, and so should we.

First, your sheer commitment in creating and planning to meet a breastfeeding goal will be one of your most powerful guiding forces. Never underestimate the power of your own will followed by a carefully constructed plan. Second and just as significant, you will need all kinds of SUPPORT! If I could recommend a breastfeeding life support kit, it would include: a more supportive bra for your enlarged milk-filled breast, support from your significant other and other care takers, support from other breastfeeding mothers so you can share stories with one another from your experiences, a lactation counselor, and a pediatrician knowledgeable about breastfeeding.

If you are fortunate enough to be home with your newborn baby, the first several weeks will be consumed with breastfeeding and trying to sleep, eat, and/or bathe at some point between feedings. Even if key people in your life do not fully understand or support your decision to breastfeed, they may be able to provide support in other ways like: changing diapers (there will be many), cleaning the house, washing clothes (and diapers if you use cloth diapers), and cooking, which may even be your dream come true, in a sense. If you are a slight control freak, like I was, it may be hard to receive this type of support in the beginning. Trust me you are not alone. Learning to receive help was one of the first of many life lessons I gained while breastfeeding that I hope to share with you throughout this book.

Entrée

In case you are wondering what is considered a reasonable breastfeeding goal, the American Academy of Pediatricians and the United States Breastfeeding Committee recommend exclusive (no other foods or drinks) breastfeeding for 6 months and breastfeeding along with food up to one year. The World Health Organization (WHO) and UNICEF also recommend 6 months of exclusive breastfeeding, but they also recommend continuing breastfeeding until the child is at least 2 years old to achieve the maximum benefit. Breastfeeding for the optimal duration, 2 years, could greatly reduce the number of deaths in children 5 years old and younger by three quarters of a million deaths each year. Think about it. Every two years over 1.5 million child deaths could be prevented from breastfeeding. Why? Breastfeeding reduces a child's risk of exposure to potentially contaminated formula and/or drinking water that can cause diarrhea, which is a worldwide leading cause of death for children 5 and under.

With my first child, I hoped to breastfeed for 2 years to match the WHO recommendations, but committed to 1 year just to give myself some grace. After I met the year mark, I reevaluated every few months. Initially, I chose a minimum of 1 year for all the many benefits of breastfeeding to both baby and mother. Breastfeeding helps to reduce the mother's risk of developing breast cancer, specifically the risk of triple negative breast cancer among African American women, helps mom lose weight, shrinks the mother's stomach faster by triggering contractions, (yes, I said contractions) and reduces the mother's risk of developing type 2 diabetes and hypertension. Simultaneously, breastfeeding reduces the baby's risk of developing obesity, diabetes, improves their cognitive ability, fosters a strong mother child bond, and so much more. Afterall, this is why breastfeeding is also called nursing - you literally are nursing yourself and your baby to health. No matter how long you decide to breastfeed, I want you to be motivated to stick to your goal.

Identify the types of support you will need for this journey and draft a plan to get it. Who are the friends and family that are in favor of your decision to breastfeed? Who are the people that just want to help? Can you make a list of the people you identified or record a voice note in your phone or tablet? Share your breastfeeding goal with the people on your list and ask them for help. You can also find a breastfeeding support group and lactation counselor in the appendix.

Refreshment

If you are anything like me, before your baby was ever born you had an idea of how you wanted their life to take shape. Did you try to guess what their features would be or who they would resemble the most? Could you have filled up several blank pages with all your speculations? But did you ever think about what your role would be in achieving the picture you had in mind?

God is no different than us when it comes to having a vivid imagination. However, God doesn't just speculate. God writes a script for each of our lives, a carefully orchestrated script, and makes sure he has a leading role in making the script a reality. God's vision of our growth and development is outlined in Jeremiah 29:11 "For I know the plans I have for you," declares the Lord, "plans to prosper you and not to harm you, plans to give you hope and a future." God sees you prosperous, hopeful, and moving toward a bright future. The only problem is that God allows all the actors in the story of your life, including you, the free will to go off script.

Just as I have invited you to draft a plan to ensure your baby will receive the best possible nutrition through your breastfeeding efforts, God, carefully, attended to every detail of your baby's life before they were born as highlighted in today's scripture: "Your eyes saw my unformed body; all the days ordained for me were written in your book before one of them came to be." So please know, you were handpicked and designed to play a leading role in your child's life, not just a leading role but a role ordained

15

by God. The word ordained is translated from a Hebrew word that means formed or fashioned, specifically the way a potter would fashion a piece of clay into a distinct vessel. Momma, you were made for this.

You may have questioned your purpose in life up to this point, but mothering this baby is definitely one of God's purposes for your life. People often say, "I wish kids came with an instruction manual." You have something even better. As you play your part, you can expect God, the director of this whole story, to give you line by line instructions.

I would like you to consider three questions today. Are you ready to accept the leading role in your child's life? Does knowing that God ordained you for this task ease any anxiety you may have about being a successful parent? Finally, will you allow God to direct you as you try to follow his script for you and your baby's life?

$\mathcal{D}ay$ 3

Got Milk?

"For you will nurse and be satisfied at her comforting breasts; you will drink deeply and delight in her overflowing abundance." -Isaiah 66:11

"Because of your father's God, who helps you, because of the Almighty, who blesses you with blessings of the skies above, blessings of the deep springs below, blessings of the breast and womb."

-Genesis 49:25

Appetizer

If you have just delivered your baby and started breastfeeding, you may be concerned about the quantity and quality of your milk. With my firstborn, after a couple of days, I was concerned about the small drops of milk coming out and wondered if the milk was sufficient because it did not seem to flow like I had imagined it would. I was aware that the first milk to be released would be the colostrum, the nutrient rich liquid filled with antibodies, which is in your breast long before you are due to deliver your baby. The colostrum is like your baby's first immunization shot, but better, of course, because there are no needles. I knew those drops were like liquid gold, however, I was still concerned about the quantity. At the time of my first pregnancy, I had not received formal training as a lactation counselor. So, I mostly relied on firsthand stories from my friends or the stories from mothers and grandmothers who participated in the research focus groups I facilitated about barriers to breastfeeding. The lack of formal training as a lactation counselor, combined with several horror stories I had heard, contributed to my confusion and unnecessary anxiety about what was happening with my breastmilk supply.

Have you ever heard the saying that "you know too much for your own good," or, "you know just enough to be dangerous?" That was my case. On the second day of my hospital stay after delivering my firstborn, my daughter, I received a visit from an older lactation counselor. She asked me, "Has your milk come in?" I was confused about the question at the time, but I responded, "Yes" because I did see droplets of milk come out. I had heard from several mothers during the focus group that they were never able to start breastfeeding because their "milk didn't come in." I assumed that my milk, indeed, had "come in," but I later learned what the lactation counselor meant, and I was wrong.

Additionally, I recognized that my daughter had lost what I thought was a decent amount of weight by the time we were supposed to be dismissed on the fourth day. She weighed 6 lbs. 1 oz. at birth and by the time of checkout, she was down to 5 lbs. 5 oz. Again, from research, I knew that breastfed infants initially lose a little more weight than formula fed infants, but I was not exactly sure how much weight loss was enough to cause concern. Before my husband and I left the hospital with my daughter, I scheduled a visit with a second lactation counselor to evaluate my latch to ensure my daughter was getting enough milk. After some manipulation, the lactation counselor said I was doing well although the latch still felt a bit painful to me. I knew to expect pain, but I wasn't sure if I could fully trust the lactation counselors' assessments because neither commented on my daughter's weight loss. To complicate matters more, I knew from formal research that many hospital staff often discriminated against women of color by providing substandard care which added to my lack of trust. While I was prepared for possible mismanagement by hospital staff, this turned out to not be my case at all.

Nevertheless, filled with facts and horror stories, I did what any "Type A" personality mother might do, I relied on all my preparation, went into trouble shooting mode, and I decided to combat my uncertainty with facts. I decided to request to use the hospital electric breast pump to measure and confirm how much breastmilk I was making. Although I had received my own electric breast pump through my insurance plan under the Affordable Care Act, I had heard and researched that the commercial grade breast pump was more powerful than the one I was given. Afterall, you can never be too sure right? Wrong!

The lactation counselor brought the breast pump in the room and set it up and asked me did I know how to use it. I said, "Yeah. I have one at home. I just wanted to practice before I left." So, she left me to myself. In a sense, I outsmarted myself. I sat with my breast connected to the pump for several moments and nothing came out. Right as I was about to freak out and get discouraged about the "confirmation" of my low milk supply the lactation counselor re-entered the room. She asked, "How's it going?" I replied, "Nothing is coming out." The lactation counselor looked at the machine, flipped a switch and said, "Maybe because you didn't turn it (the suction level) up high enough." After that quick move, some milk began to come out. I said "Oh, ok thanks, maybe that's why I should have read the instruction manual before starting." Go ahead, you can laugh at me because I do when I recount these stories. A side note for first time breastfeeding mothers: using a breast pump for the sole purpose of measuring your milk supply is not recommended because it may cause unnecessary anxiety like I experienced.

Sure, it was normal for me to want the best possible start to my breastfeeding journey. Yes, it was normal to desire to gain as much momentum as possible toward what I expected to be an uphill battle to successfully breastfeed my daughter. Yet, in my imaginary fight to protect my right to breastfeed my daughter against all the odds stacked up against Black mothers and with the assistance of all the prescription drugs and postpartum hormones circulating through my body, I was becoming a made-up superhero: Black Super Mom. I needed to return to the folk wisdom of my people who say "take a chill pill" which is another way to say calm down.

Entrée

Since the birth of my daughter, I have received lactation counseling training and learned that my daughter's weight loss was not significant, nor was my supply of breastmilk inadequate. My daughter had wet diapers and eventually had a "blowout" diaper in her father's arms as we were being dismissed from the hospital. Wet and poopy diapers are the more accurate indications that a baby is receiving milk. Nothing can come out if nothing is going in.

Without the proper training, I was unaware of a few technical terms like "milk coming in" and how having a cesarean section (C-section) would impact my milk supply AND my baby's weight loss. Research shows that most babies lose a little weight after birth and exclusively breastfed infants tend to lose a little more weight than formula-fed babies. Yet, by the six-month mark, exclusively breastfed infants no longer show any deficits in growth. There may be a need for iron and Vitamin D supplements in exclusively breastfed infants, but otherwise, there is no evidence of malnutrition among exclusively breastfed infants. Additionally, moms who have C-sections, like I did, receive a lot of fluids that may also reach the baby. In this case, the baby is born a little larger than they would have been at birth because of the fluid. In my case, some of my daughter's weight loss was due to her shedding some of that fluid and not solely due to my breastmilk supply.

There are two phases of breastmilk. The first phase of breastmilk is called colostrum or first milk, which quickly transitions to the more abundant mature breastmilk after delivery. Factors such as premature birth, medications given during labor and delivery, especially during c-sections, or incomplete removal of the placenta, can delay the transition of the early breastmilk (colostrum) from transitioning to the more abundant mature breastmilk supply. These problems are usually temporary and correctable with the appropriate intervention.

I later learned that this milk transition process was what the lactation counselor meant when she asked about my milk "coming in." While I had the colostrum prior to delivery, my breastmilk didn't transition to mature milk until after I arrived home from the hospital. The delay was most likely due to my emergency C-section, where I received extremely strong drugs including general anesthesia, ephedra to reverse the rapid drop in my blood pressure, and a morphine equivalent. However, there was no mistaking when the mature milk supply "came in" because all a sudden, my breasts felt like they were filled with concrete. My breasts were so enlarged that I could see the green vessels. My husband's eyes bulged when he saw me. He was happy, but I was uncomfortable. The proper term is engorged. This was relieved by taking a warm shower and feeding my daughter. Afterall, I had milk!

Whether you only have your early milk, the colostrum, or your mature milk supply, you've got milk! If you are concerned about your baby's weight and/or your milk supply do not try to fix anything on your own. If you have a lactation counselor or a pediatrician who is knowledgeable about breastfeeding, they will know the amount of weight loss that needs intervention. If supply is truly an issue, these professionals will know safe and proven ways to stimulate your milk supply or recommend alternative feeding solutions. In the meantime, here's a nugget of wisdom. Frequent on demand feeding is the best way to increase your breastmilk supply. Regular stimulation of your breast from your baby's touch and even your baby's cry will help your body produce breastmilk.

If your baby was born premature or needed to be admitted to the neonatal intensive care unit (NICU) for any reason, you may be wondering what to do about your breastmilk. Your breastmilk can help save your premature baby's life. Premature infants cannot handle the proteins in formula, but they can handle your breastmilk. One option is to express your breastmilk by hand or with a manual or electric breast pump that can be transferred to a cup or bottled used to feed your baby. If you are in the hospital, the hospital can let you borrow a breast pump, and like an old hit song says, "It's electric!" Alternatively, the Affordable Care Act mandates all federal insurance providers to provide free breast pumps, or you can contact your local WIC (Women, Infants and Children) clinic to gain access to a breast pump.

Refreshment

Not only do infants need their mother's milk, but adults need the milk of the Word of God. The Bible describes the Word of God as milk. 1Peter 2:2 states "like newborn babies, long for the pure milk of the word, so that by it you may grow in respect to salvation." As mother's milk does a physical body good, the spiritual milk of the Word of God found in the Bible does a spiritual body good. Have you had your milk today? It is essential to your spiritual, mental, emotional and physical health every day.

Can you make sure to schedule time to nurture yourself with the word of God and other healthy habits? The time spent reading or listening to the Bible, does not need to be lengthy, elaborate or necessarily formally scheduled. You may have to just go with flow, and yes, the pun is intended. Just be sure to get it done daily.

For me, my quiet time is in the restroom in the morning because it seems to be the only place and time where I find peace and quiet. I learned this lesson from fathers. Have you ever wondered how they seem to escape to the restroom and stay locked away at just the right stressful time? Let me get back on track. I either bring the physical Bible with me to read for a few minutes, or I use the Bible app on my phone or tablet which has daily devotionals and inspiring scriptural quotes. Also, this app allows me to do topical searches for things like anxiety, faith, forgiveness etc. Experiment with different options until you find something that works for you. Here's an inspiring quote for today. John 4:14 speaking of Jesus says "but whoever drinks of the water that I will give him (or her) shall never thirst; but the water that I will give him (or her) will become in him (or her) a well of water springing up to eternal life. Talk about refreshment. Mom I pray that you become so refreshed that your soul becomes a wellspring of life!

Day 4

Mind the Latch.

"I am the LORD your God, who brought you up out of Egypt. Open wide your mouth and I will fill it." - Psalm 81:10

Appetizer

Have you ever heard the saying "a closed mouth doesn't get fed"? That is an ultimate truth of breastfeeding. A good latch begins with your baby's mouth wide open, and the latch is one of the most important factors of breastfeeding success. On the flip side, a shallow or weaker latch, is a leading cause of breastfeeding discomfort and low breastmilk supply.

As a result of all the drugs from my c-section, my firstborn was very drowsy her first week of life, and I became concerned that she was not waking enough to feed. So, I reached out to an experienced breastfeeding mother for help, who suggested that I rub my nipple against my daughter's mouth to entice her to feed. However, my mom friend did not warn me that my daughter would be so enticed to feed that she would quickly clamp down on my nipple like an alligator before I could get more of my breast in her mouth. My daughter had a shallow latch, and it was painful.

This shallow latch often leads to inadequate milk transfer, or you experience enough pain to stop the feeding early. What does your latch have to do with your milk supply? Your body tightly regulates its resources, carefully matching supply with demand. So, the less milk you release the less your body will produce.

How do you achieve a good latch that will lead to an abundant milk supply? Start with a wide-open mouth. You want the baby's mouth to open to an angle of 145 degrees or more. This allows most of your areola, the dark part around your nipple, to fill the baby's mouth. The baby's suction will

28

stimulate milk release by pressing on the maximum amount of milk ducts. As your nipple extends into the baby's mouth, milk gushes in. A great exchange occurs and you, subsequently, have satisfied your baby with good things. This sounds easier than it is to achieve. I learned the hard way, so you don't have to.

Entrée

To achieve a wide-open mouth position, timing is critical. First, it is important to start the feeding while the baby is still calm. If your baby is doing that deep guttural cry, most likely you have waited too long to feed the baby and the baby has become "hangry." Little ones have no patience once they are hangry often resulting in them swiftly clamping down on your nipple once it is near. The end result will be a shallow and painful latch. While some milk will still transfer with the shallow latch, the baby will work extra hard in the form of forceful sucking motions trying to get the nipple to extend fully into their mouths which triggers the milk release. The baby then becomes frustrated and often gives up feeding before they are satisfied, or rather, filled. I will provide strategies on how to troubleshoot that dynamic in the next chapter, but for now let's focus on how to avoid that dynamic by feeding the baby before "hanger" sets in. Therefore, you need to learn your baby's feeding cues, so you can identify them and intervene early.

Feeding cues are frequent eye movements when the baby is still asleep but on the verge of waking, mouthing movements where the baby begins to suck air, or when the baby starts gnawing on their fingers, hands, or whatever is nearby. If you bring the baby near you (belly to belly) and place your nipple above the baby's nose, normally the baby will turn their head toward your breast and open their mouth wide to latch on. Did you notice I said, put your nipple on their nose not on their mouth? Babies smell your milk and open their mouth wide like an alligator. And just like an alligator, a baby's clamp down is swift. Remember, I learned this firsthand.

When you start with your nipple on the baby's nose, their mouth will land on your areola and not the nipple. Your baby will have hit the target. With this good latch, the baby will normally drink until satisfied peacefully releasing your breast when they are finished, and you can have a sigh of relief. You scored one for the team. You moved the ball into the in-zone. Good job! I played sports, so I often use sports analogies. May I add that breastfeeding often feels like a sport in the early days, and it is surely medal worthy.

Refreshment

Mom, do you notice any similarities in your personal journey to fulfillment? A closed mouth does not get fed. Do you open your mouth wide in prayer and let God know that you hunger or thirst and expect him to fulfill you? Or do you proverbially open your mouth a little bit by making only selective prayer requests, while reserving all other issues to figure out and solve on your own? Or, in impatience and frustration, do you seek to fill yourself with whatever is the closest thing you can get your hands on to pacify the hunger pains and forego asking God altogether? The extent of God directly showing Himself in your life will be in direct proportion to how widely and deeply you open your mouth in prayer. Maybe you have a history of unmet needs where it seemed like no one noticed your hunger cues until you were raving mad or crying out for help. Even when people finally attended to your needs, maybe you found their response inadequate in meeting those needs.

Take this time and opportunity as you learn to respond to the feeding cues of your baby, to allow God to respond to your feeding cues. Unlike your infant, you are not forced to cry or scream in frustration as your only form of communication to experience the nurture of an available, willing, and capable God. God will notice your needs before you even ask. Matthew 6:8 says, "God knows what you need before you ask" and plans to supply it. All you need to do is open your mouth wide by asking in prayer for everything you need and desire and wait for God to deliver a suitable solution according to his masterplan for your life. This is how you learn that God is both able and reliable to take care of you.

Day 5

Confronting the Hangry Baby

"But you, son of man, listen to what I say to you. Do not rebel like that rebellious people; open your mouth and eat what I give you." -Ezekiel 2:8

Appetizer

On day 3, I talked about starting a breastfeeding session by noticing and responding to the baby's feeding cues early while the baby is still calm. Yet inevitably life will happen, and there will come a time when you won't be able to notice the baby's feeding cues and you will miss the baby's self-imposed feeding deadline. Maybe you'll be in another room, like the bathroom when you finally find time to take a bath. Maybe you will be attending to another child, doing work, or out running an errand when your baby is ready to feed. Whatever the case may be, the baby will be doing the hangry cry. No make that the pissed-off cry. I'll never forget, when my mom first described my 2-week-old daughter as "pissed." I was like "Mom, what do you mean pissed? She's a baby. I'm sure something must be seriously wrong for her to cry like that." My mom did not budge on her assessment and responded, "No. She's [my daughter] just pissed you're taking too long to feed her." What kind of words of comfort were those to a new mother? Yet, I trusted in my mom's wisdom. My mom is one of the sweetest most encouraging people ever. However, at that moment, my mom's encouragement came in the form of a much-needed revelation: my baby was hangry.

A peculiar thing happens when newborns become hangry. My daughter would get so hungry that she would scream to the top of her lungs. But, when I pulled out my breast, she would move her head and neck backwards and away from my breast. The struggle began as I tried to the get my breast in her mouth to supply the food she was looking for, but she kept pulling away in her hollering fit. The neck muscles of infants are so strong. Gone away was the idea of this tiny infant being super fragile and possibly broken with the subtlest move. I was in a full-on wrestling match with a 4-day old child trying to shove my breast in her mouth.

By that point, I had discovered that under normal circumstances when my daughter was not hangry, she had a shallow latch and clamped down as soon as the nipple got in her sight. For me, the wrestling match was a lifesaver. When my daughter revved back in one of those full on shrills, her mouth was wide open. I used it as an opportunity to get a good portion of my breast in her mouth providing a more productive feeding session. Hence, I had won the match and so did my daughter.

Entrée

While I did the best I could then, lactation training has shown me a better way. The best way to begin a feeding session with a hangry baby is through calming and comforting the baby. The best way to calm the baby is to bring them close to you either on your belly or laying them on your chest and if possible, make direct "skin to skin" contact with your baby by removing any clothing barriers. Newborns understand loving touch so much better than words. A calm baby will be more patient with you. It will be a much more comfortable feeding session for you as well. Please note that your partner can even contribute to calming the baby using the skin-to-skin method, while you prepare yourself to feed the baby.

Your infant is much like you in that they were not born with patience. They have been in the comfort of your womb and probably never experienced a hunger pain. Food was always readily available to them with a pull of the cord. Even if you had not eaten, the baby would, even if your body had to resort to breaking down your muscle and bones to supply the baby what it needed. That is why maternal nutrition is so important during pregnancy and while breastfeeding. Nature's design preserves the baby, and you have to preserve yourself when it comes to nutrition.

Do not be discouraged if any effort you put forward seems too slow compared to the instant environment of the womb. It may be hard at first, but don't allow your baby's frustration to frustrate you. If you can be calm, it will transfer to your baby. Just like you had to learn patience, your baby will learn to be patient and, more importantly, not to resist the gift they so desperately need: your nourishment in the form of breastmilk.

Refreshment

Can you see yourself in your newborn's disposition? I surely could see myself in my firstborn. Oh, I throw a full-on temper tantrum when God takes too long, or at least what I perceive as too long to provide what I need. Then, when God does show up, often I am so irritated that I fight my own blessing and act disinterested.

If people have labeled you a diva, or they have suggested you blow smoke through your nose or you come off as intimidating, maybe you aren't angry but just hangry from your unmet needs like your baby. Often when we women express our needs with passion, we are dismissed as "just being too emotional." Gender specific stereotypes limit women's expression of negative emotions to crying, which is considered weakness or being "too sensitive," while reserving expressions of anger for men. Just look at childhood dramatic play. Toy characters marketed to girls, until recently, have been soft spoken and gentle, and toy characters marketed to boys have strong voices and use force. Women who dare to violate this social norm by expressing dissatisfaction or disgust with strong emotion, also known as anger, are often penalized by being labeled a curse word that means female dog or the more euphemistic term "diva."

Unfortunately, one whole race of women has been diminished in this way and given their own version of the "being too emotional" or "diva" label. African American women have been branded as "angry black women," as if their anger is a character trait instead of the byproduct of their disproportionate level of distressing experiences that are well documented in all kinds of research journals.

A famous candy bar company took advantage of the concept of the "diva" and "angry black woman." In the candy company's series of "hangry" commercials, one commercial showed 4 people riding in a car and all were supposed to be men. With one exception, the "hangry" man, originally appeared as a musical diva, Aretha Franklin the Queen of Soul, and acted very demanding and even popped the guy in front of her in the head. Afterwards, the guy sitting next to her insists that she eats the candy bar, which transformed Aretha Franklin back into an ordinary calm white man. Before the commercial ended, one of the guys in the front began to get irritable and hangry and transforms into another musical diva Liza Minnelli. What contrast and irony! Maybe the candy company isn't just exploiting a negative stereotype about women and minorities, but maybe they are revealing an overlooked truth: hunger is often disguised as anger.

Though people may walk around you like they are walking on eggshells, God is not intimidated by you and knows how to handle you. In God's eyes you resemble a baby with unmet needs. In a previous chapter, I referenced the scripture 1 Peter 2:2 "Like newborn babies crave the milk of the word." How do newborn babies express their cravings? They cry. Your newborn is a perfect example of how effective crying out can be. They cry and you hurry to feed them.

My sister, no matter what your background or what society says about crying, have you forgotten how to cry out to God about your unmet needs? Like any good parent, God will respond to your cry. I surely had and only recognized it when I began writing this chapter. Anger was more familiar. I talked/vented to God often, but I rarely cried. I needed nourishment sure, but first I needed to be calmed.

Just as I described how my breastfeeding battle with my hangry child could have been resolved with a soothing touch, God can calm each of our "hangry" behaviors with a simple touch. Because God represents an authority figure, I know many of you may cringe at the thought of being touched by an authority figure, especially, if the touches you experienced from them, whether parents, teachers, coaches, or religious leaders were inappropriate, abusive, or as in my case just absent sometimes. But dear heart you were created to be touched lovingly, and dare I say you need it. It is what separates humans from the animal kingdom. While God used words to bring the rest of creation into existence, God reached down and formed us with His hands. Touch is vital to our existence.

How does God touch us? Isaiah 41:9-10 says "I took you from the ends of the earth, from its farthest corners I called you. I said, 'You are my servant' I have chosen you and have not rejected you. So do not fear, for I am with you; do not be dismayed, for I am your God. I will strengthen you and help you; I will uphold you with my righteous right hand." Zephaniah 3:17 states, "The Lord your God is with you, the Mighty warrior who saves. He will take great delight in you; in his love he will no longer rebuke you but will rejoice over you with singing." God touches our spirit and soul through words of affirmation written in the Bible, by showing us how much we are thought of, by delivering us from dangerous circumstances, by singing over us and allowing us to experience peace when we hear songs about God.

If you resist God's touch at first while you learn to trust God's intentions, God will persist through your resistance. As we decide to fight to breastfeed our babies despite their resistance, God fights to bless us despite ours. If the analogy sounds exaggerated, there is a recorded account in the book of Genesis in the Bible of God manifesting as a man who wrestles with a man named Jacob. Genesis 32: 24-27 says "Jacob was left alone, and a man wrestled with him till daybreak." Then the man said, "Let me go, for it is daybreak." When the man saw that he could not overpower him [Jacob], he touched the socket of Jacob's hip so that his hip was wrenched as he wrestled with the man. But Jacob replied, "I will not let you go unless you bless me." The man asked him, "What is your name?" "Jacob," he answered. Then the man said, "Your name will no longer be Jacob, but Israel, because you have struggled with God and with humans and have overcome."

Jacob's wrestling ended when he was touched by God and blessed. Not only did the wrestling match change Jacob's physical body, but his name changed from Jacob, meaning heel catcher or trickster, to Israel meaning wrestles with God or triumphant with God. Jacob's name change indicated a character shift from scheming and manipulating in attempt to meet his own needs and desires to triumphantly obtaining God's blessing and favor. As a matter of fact, Jacob was so shady that he schemed his own twin brother out of his inheritance rights in exchange for a meal, but even that relationship was reconciled after Jacob received what he needed from God through the wrestling match. So can you!

In your own life are you grabbing hold or pushing away from the blessing of God? Today, God's physical touch often happens through experiences with people who believe in Jesus. The Bible describes these people as "the body of Christ" or what some call "the Church." Literally, the believers represent the hands of God in this earth. Are there people in your life who are trying to supply you with resources that only God knows you need, but you don't know if you can trust them? Instead, you pull away. Don't worry, if these people are legit, they will be patient with you and be willing to win your trust, but are you willing to receive what they are offering? You may find that it is God trying to reach out to you through them.

Dessert

As a teen, my parents, who had been very loving and doting during my childhood, were going through a divorce and they became more and more emotionally withdrawn and visibly burdened. Therefore, I stopped seeking affectionate touch from them and really anyone else. Then, in college, I sought stability and community by joining a college church group that I now believe was a bit one sided in its teachings about physical touch. The ministry overly emphasized how touch could basically lead to sex. We all have probably learned at this point that sex and affectionate touch are not the same. Even if people are sexually active, it doesn't mean they are receiving affectionate touch. Nevertheless, in the name of full devotion to God, I abandoned all forms of physical touch except a handshake or a quick side hug. Yes, it kept me far from sexually inappropriate interactions until I got married, but I was missing something. I was no longer vulnerable which made me feel in control, but I was not in touch with my true emotions. A firestorm of unexpressed needs was brewing beneath the surface. In many ways God by His mercy and grace has used my husband's loving touch to help unlock places in my heart and soul that needed nurturing.

I hope my story encourages you to welcome the loving touch of another person in your life. It may just be the source of comfort you have been missing.

Day 6

You Won't Forget to Feed the Baby

"Can a mother forget the baby at her breast and have no compassion on the child she has borne? Though she may forget, I will not forget you!" – Isaiah 49:15

Appetizer

I was a breastfeeding researcher and advocate before I ever had my first child. I heard stories of how time-consuming breastfeeding could be compared to formula feeding. During focus groups, participants not in favor of breastfeeding perceived those breastfed infants were not getting fed enough, suggesting breastmilk was inadequate. On the contrary, advocates implied that the breastfed babies just needed to feed more often, and some unaware mothers simply did not feed their babies enough. Breastfeeding opponents also painted the picture of the breastfed babies they observed as frail, clingy, skinny babies that were crying all the time out of hunger. My own family has said similar things when another family member was one of the first to breastfeed their child. "The baby cries all the time because she must be hungry," they said.

So, I prepared myself to overcome this challenge of having a starving baby by setting the alarm on my iPhone to go off every 1 hour and 45 minutes. I thought my daughter would need to eat every two hours and I wanted to be prepared and ahead of the game so I set the alarm 15 minutes early to ensure I would not forget. This is laughable looking back.

At that time, I did not realize that my daughter would not let her hunger go unnoticed in those first days if she were hungry. Plus, I forgot the child would pretty much eat around the clock. When was I going to find time to sleep? As soon as I got into a deep sleep the alarm clock was going off. I did not forget to feed the baby, but I did almost drop her in that first week as I fell asleep and relaxed my arm while she was doing her 7th or 8th feeding of the day or night whichever it was.

Entrée

Research, indeed, does support more frequent feedings for breastfed babies because the mother's milk is easier to digest and goes through the baby faster. While a formula fed baby may feed every 4 hours, a breastfed infant may feed every two hours. The timing is not as important as feeding the baby when they give you cues. This may result in 10-12 daily feedings.

Now, if you have twins, especially identical twins, it is possible in this early stage that you did forget to feed one twin and fed the other twin twice. I'll never forget when a friend of mine, who was an identical twin, shared a story about how his mom fed his twin brother twice instead of him. His mother only discovered the error once he screamed nonstop. To overcome this, his mother put different colored bracelets on the babies. The same strategy might work for mothers of multiples beyond twins. Also, if you are forgetful, you may try keeping a feeding log.

At this point, let me interject some much-needed encouragement here. Your baby is growing. As the baby grows, their stomach gets bigger, meaning they hold more milk at one time and need to eat less often. You will not be a continuous breastmilk faucet forever, maybe just for the first 6 weeks. Eventually, the pace will become more reasonable. You are establishing your breastmilk supply and feeding routine. You will sleep, eat, bathe, and talk to adults again. Let me say it one more time, you will sleep again!

Refreshment

Relax, you will not forget to feed your baby. And more importantly, God will not forget to take care of you providing what you need at just the right time. I was afraid to fall asleep on the job, but God never sleeps nor slumbers and doesn't need an alarm clock. You will never become too heavy with your needs that God's arm will falter and drop you like I almost did with my daughter. Isaiah 40:28 states, "Do you not know? Have you not heard? The Lord is the everlasting God, the Creator of the ends of the earth. He will not grow tired or weary, and his understanding no one can fathom." In fact, like any good mother, God is awake and anticipating your need.

Have you told God what you need in your life? Does it appear that God has forgotten about you because of how long you have been waiting? Or does it appear that God is too busy meeting the needs of others around you, so you have begun to reason that your needs might not be as important as everyone else's, so why bother God with them? If it seems like God has forgotten about your need, consider making a remembrance log either physically or electronically of all the ways God has met your needs in the past? I have found that practice helps me to remain patient when I grow weary of waiting.

Secondly, when people in your life get something that you were desiring, do you celebrate their blessing as a sign of hope that God is still able to meet your needs? Or have you been taught that resources are scarce, and life is about survival of the fittest, thus we must compete for the few available resources? Maybe you think God is like my twin friend's mother who cannot distinguish between you and the next person, so somehow God delivered your package to your friend or family's address instead of yours. If you've been taught either of these concepts directly or indirectly, it may feel like someone else took your portion.

This frustration will often manifest in the form of envy. I know from experience. All these situations are challenging and make it hard to keep waiting on God. But the truth I have learned is God is not limited in resources, is willing to meet the needs of all that call on Him and will keep shelling out the needs until everyone is satisfied. God's provision is not a first come first serve offer like many retail promotions that say, "limited while supplies last." God is waiting to fulfill every legitimate need you have with something good.

Are there any blessings in your current situation that may have gone unnoticed because they took longer than desired to arrive? Can you take a moment today to meditate on that blessing, which is a fulfillment of a need or desire? Then, in your gratitude for that blessing, eliminate any lingering frustration or bitterness from the wait. Take time to reflect upon any ways you may have grown during your waiting period. I lovingly, yet strongly, encourage you to take time to do both.

Day 7

Let It flow!

"For you will nurse and be satisfied at her comforting breasts; you will drink deeply and delight in her overflowing abundance." -Isaiah 66:11

Appetizer

By the time I birthed my second child, I had overcome many of the breastfeeding challenges I encountered with my firstborn - an insufficient latch, getting a good holding position, knowing when to feed, and milking both breasts equally, so now, the milk was just flowing. My son, who was born at 37 weeks and considered premature, latched on like a pro. All the lactation counselors were amazed, as they were already preparing me for breastfeeding issues and expected weight loss due to his prematurity. Yet, when it was time for me to check out of the hospital, they could not believe he lost only one ounce. At birth my son weighed 5 lbs. 10 oz which was less than my daughter who was 6lbs. 1oz., but by the time my son left the hospital he weighed more than my daughter did at the same point, which was 5lbs. 9 oz. versus her 5 lbs. 5 oz. He also was born via C-section but lost only a total of 1 ounce during that first week. Even more, my son stunned the pediatrician when he weighed 10 lbs. by his 1-month visit. He skipped from preemie clothes to age 3-months clothing with quickness.

It was a relief to know that my son was a breastfeeding pro, but the extra milk was a little bit of a nuisance. I was dripping milk in between feedings, so I decided to pump my breastmilk to develop a supply for when I had to be away by the second week. Remember, for breastfeeding moms and babies, breastmilk is like liquid gold so it is hard to see the breastmilk fall to the ground, or on your shirt, or on the shower wall, unused, but I could not keep up with the pace of feeding and pumping. I also forgot to mention that my let down (the initial release of breastmilk after stimulation) was fast, and often my son was hosed in the forehead and eye with my milk before I could get it in his mouth. I felt like I was drowning my son as the milk came squirting out. As this continued, I decided to consult with a lactation counselor, who explained how I had an overabundance of breastmilk, and my pumping was adding to the situation. The solution was to slow my breastmilk supply down which involved stopping the pumping and dealing with some engorgement. I would have donated the milk, but I assumed I was unable because of a medication I was taking to prevent blood clots. This highlights an important point about medicines. If you are worried, like I was, about any prescription drug or supplement passing through your breastmilk to your baby, please use the Lactmed website provided in the appendix to know for sure.

Entrée

If you have a lot of breastmilk coming in, rejoice in your abundant supply because some women have a supply that is lower. Before I go any further, you must purchase a pair of nursing pads ASAP unless you want to look like you entered a wet T-shirt contest and won! The slightest things can make your milk flow. However, if you have an oversupply, it can be uncomfortable as I just described. If you desire to slow down the milk supply, you must rest and resist the urge to keep on feeding or pumping your milk, unless you plan on storing or donating the extra breastmilk. If you need to return to work soon, you may choose to pump or express your milk to store and freeze for later. Alternatively, you may consider donating the excess to a milk bank. You can find the nearest milk bank to you by contacting an organization called HMBANA (Human Milk Bank Association of North America) which is listed in the appendix.

Refreshment

I learned a life lesson, as you release what you have, more will come. This not only applies to breastmilk, but all that God wants to abundantly bring into your life. Do you want abundance? Then release the gifts you have freely received and more will come freely to you. Do you wish you had more talents? Use the talents you already have. Would you like more finances? Then properly invest the money you have. This not only applies to physical gifts and talents, but interpersonal resources. If you want forgiveness, grant it to others. If you need mercy, be merciful to others. Afterall, we just observed how painful withholding can be. I will conclude with a scripture that is often quoted in churches across America especially during offering time, which is Luke 6:38. However, when this scripture is read in the context of the preceding verse 37, it clearly outlines a recipe for achieving inner peace and best illustrates today's concept of flow.

Luke 6:37 states, "Do not judge, and you will not be judged. Do not condemn, and you will not be condemned. Forgive, and you will be forgiven." Verse thirty-eight, which is the popular verse goes on to say, "Give, and it will be given to you. A good measure, pressed down, shaken together and running over, will be poured into your lap. For with the measure you use, it will be measured to you."- Luke 6:37-38. So, Momma, let it flow!

Day 8

A Milk Donor Can Be a God Send.

"Kings will be your foster fathers, and their queens your nursing mothers. They will bow to you face down and lick the dust at your feet. Then you will know that I am the LORD; those who hope in Me will never be put to shame." -Isaiah 49:23

"Our desire is not that other might be relieved while you are hard pressed, but that there might be equality. At the present time, your plenty will supply what they need, so that in turn their plenty will supply what you need. The goal is equality, as it is written: "The one who gathered much did not have too much, and the one who gathered little did not have too little." -2Corinthians 8:13-15

Appetizer

Some mothers have enough milk to share with others, while others are not able to supply enough breastmilk for their babies. Therefore, milk banks were created. But long before there were breast pumps and bottles to store milk or professional organizations to manage the milk donation process, there were wet nurses.

Throughout cultures around the world, wet nurses were women of all ethnic backgrounds who breastfed other women's children, often coming from a lower social or economic class than the family that employed them. In places like North and South America, many wet nurses of African descent were enslaved by the families they served. After slavery ended in the USA, African American wet nurses, were stereotypically depicted by the "Mammy" character in film and television. To note, the first African American woman who ever won an Oscar award, was Hattie McDaniel for her role as Mammy in *Gone with the Wind*.

Aunt Jemima, the pancake brand character, is the longest lasting fictional depiction of a mammy. I say fictional because "mammy" is portrayed as overweight, loyal to her mistress, and happy to attend to the master's children and their needs at the expense of her own family. While these ladies may have been loyal, they were not likely to have been overweight because masters often malnourished their slaves. Like most women, they also had maternal desires to nurture their own children who either had to be neglected or brought along. The real-life stories of African American wet nurses' heroism are more fascinating and is worthy of much more acclaim than Hollywood's depiction of mammy.

Entrée

Wet nurses have played critical roles throughout history, especially during public health crises, and we are currently experiencing two of the most devastating public health crises to date: the COVID-19 and HIV/AIDS pandemics. During the yellow fever epidemic in Philadelphia, PA in 1793, nurses from the Free African Society, helped save orphaned and abandoned infants by breastfeeding them in addition to caring for the sick when the white elite fled the city and others refused to help.[5] Notably, several of these women served at the former home of Andrew Hamilton after it was converted into a makeshift hospital called Bush Hill. At the time Philadelphia, was the capitol of the United States of America, so if the city had crumbled it is possible that the United States never would have gained the prominence it has today. The African American women in Philadelphia are only one example of the countless wet nurses throughout history who were not

---

[5] Jones, A., Allen, R., American Imprint Collection, Marian S. Carson Collection, Joseph Meredith Toner Collection & Ebenezer Hazard Pamphlet Collection. (1794) A narrative of the proceedings of the black people, during the late awful calamity in Philadelphia, in the year: and a refutation of some censures thrown upon them in some late publications. Philadelphia: Printed for the authors, by William W. Woodward. [Pdf]

considered queens during their day, but who I believe are worthy of royal status for saving their nations.

Wet nursing was not just relegated to work for hire or the forcible exploitation of slave women's bodies, but according to one researcher, women of all races formed "informal networks of support where women shared their breast milk."[6] The latter would be most equivalent to modern day milk banking.

You may have intended to breastfeed but find yourself temporarily unable due to severe illness, malnourishment, or dealing with an insufficient milk supply, yet you have a premature newborn (preemie) that needs the milk to survive. Your premature baby's best chance at life besides your prayers, love, and medical care is human milk. Preemie babies' digestive and respiratory systems are often not mature enough to process formula. Additionally, some mothers who have contracted HIV may be advised by their medical provider not to breastfeed to prevent transmitting the virus through breastmilk. Yet the guidance may vary depending upon whether the mother is receiving antiretroviral therapy or not. So, if this scenario applies to you consult with your medical provider. Yet no matter the reason that has caused you to need a donation of breastmilk, many mothers who have an overly abundant milk supply donate for this very purpose. Fortunately, most of these women do not have to do so at the expense of their own children unlike

---

[6] West, E., & Knight, R. J. (2017). Mothers' milk: Slavery, wet-nursing, and black and white women in the antebellum south. Journal of Southern History, 83(1), 37-68.

many wet nurses in the past. I say most women because there is an emerging trend where mothers, whose babies were stillborn or died before age one, courageously continue to pump their breastmilk and donate what they pump. In this context, the milk donation may provide a glimmer of hope and therapy during a time of immense disappointment by allowing the mother to continue to contribute to the cycle of life.

If you have consulted with a doctor or lactation counselor and still have a small supply of milk or they determined you are ineligible to breastfeed, you may consider finding out if you are eligible to utilize donations from a milk bank. The milk bank sterilizes the milk before it is distributed. Remember, if you trust cow's milk to be compatible with your baby, you can have more confidence in the human milk from another mother.

Maybe you are the mom with the abundant milk supply. If so, have you considered donating your excess? If you are from a minority community, donating your breastmilk may be revolutionary for you or a form of reclamation. Unlike many of our foremothers, you have an opportunity to use your God given resources for the betterment of your own community. No matter what your ethnic background or nationality, you could become the Queen Mother to some child fighting for a chance at this life. Let God use you!

Dessert

Here is a sweet story to emphasize today's concept. My cousin, Jamila, had a premature daughter, born 25 weeks gestation, who remained in the NICU for 3 months. Although Jamila was initially not able to breastfeed her daughter, Saree, at the breast, she expressed her milk with a breast pump. Because Jamila knew pumping her breastmilk was a matter of her daughter's survival, she was faithful to pump her breastmilk. In fact, Jamila had so much milk that she donated some to a milk bank to help other babies like Saree. Once Saree was released from the hospital, Jamila was able to feed her directly from her breast to the amazement of doctors and nurses, who believed Saree would have "nipple confusion" and fail to latch after being fed with a bottle for so long. More amazingly, Saree did not suffer any of the complications that many preterm infants face, like asthma or cognitive delays. Instead, Saree is brilliant, has started two different businesses, is writing her first novel, and she is only 15! Her mother credits it to breastfeeding, and I would add exceptional nurturing and parenting.

Refreshment

Mother, whatever you need, trust that God can use resources outside your own means to meet your needs. Do not be ashamed of your lack. Let me repeat that, do not be ashamed of your lack. Your insufficiency linked with hope in God can open the door to a miracle. If you can, write down your needs and then create a list of people and organizations you know that may be able to help with those needs. If your mind is blank, the internet can be your best friend. Type something like "organizations that supply diapers in your city," in the search engine of your choice. You will be surprised how many organizations are dedicated to helping meet the needs of people, including the needs of moms and babies. Even if you do not see your specific need, always make your request known to God and watch him fulfill it as he sees fit by bringing people and resources into your life you never imagined possible.

Day 9

Ouch! My Breast or Nipples Hurt

*"Looking unto Jesus the author and perfecter of our faith, who for the joy that was set before him **endured the cross**, despising shame, and hath sat down at the right hand of the throne of God."* - Hebrews 12: 2

*"For this light momentary **affliction** is preparing for us an eternal weight of glory beyond all comparison, as we look not to the things that are seen but to the things that are unseen. For the things that are seen **are transient**, but the things that are unseen are eternal."*- 2 Corinthian 4: 17-18

Dessert

What do those Bible verses have to do with breastfeeding and motherhood? Everything! Those verses talk about pain and affliction. There is pain in parenting and God knows that firsthand. Just as there was some pain and discomfort during pregnancy and labor, there can be some in breastfeeding. I would not be fair to you if I suggested that you may not experience some pain along the breastfeeding journey. So, I am flipping the script here. I will start at the end of the story instead of the prelude. The solution for any instance of pain experienced during motherhood is in this verse: "Fix your eyes on Jesus, who Himself fixed his eyes on the JOY set before him." The antidote to pain is JOY!

Appetizer

Ironically, we call little babies bundles of JOY. Although, in their infant and embryonic state, they have probably caused us the most pain we have ever experienced to date. Did we forget back pain, pelvic pain, and nausea during pregnancy? Did we forget contractions, and the trauma to the birth canal? Yes and no. We do remember some of those pains, but the joy of seeing a breathing, kicking soul overrides it all. You must think of your breastfeeding pain the same way. It will not last forever and the benefits of breastfeeding your baby will be lasting. This solemn thought will help you to endure.

Entrée

Would you be surprised to discover that pain during breastfeeding was the number one stated reason mothers and grandmothers who were initially excited about breastfeeding discontinued breastfeeding earlier than planned among focus group participants? I am not trying to minimize the pain any mother may experience because I experienced my fair share from nipple chapping, engorgement, and being bitten. I even needed steroid injections in my hand because of a condition called mommy thumb, which is similar to carpel tunnel syndrome, because I was holding my daughter the wrong way. I am here to give you encouragement that pain can be overcome and, in many cases, AVOIDED.

So, let us specifically talk about the pain some women encounter during breastfeeding. Most often, the pain is resulting from a poor latch. But in some less frequent cases, the nipple discomfort can be a sign of illness like mastitis or a result of flat or inverted nipples, which would need treatment by a medical provider. I will not expound on the latter reasons for breast and nipple discomfort here because those need direct evaluation by a trained lactation counselor or medical provider. Rather, I will address the latch and positioning because they are the most common reasons for discomfort. Please refer to the appendix to help identify a lactation counselor near you.

A whole chapter has been dedicated to achieving a productive latch: "Day 4: Mind the Latch".

So, let us talk about posture. The baby could be positioned too far away from the mother, which would create a strained feeding position for both mother and baby. When the baby is not skin-to-skin, the latch will normally be superficial meaning the baby did not get a good portion of the areola in their mouth and clamps down only on the nipple. This can be painful for the mother. Secondly, mom will normally be slumped over, creating a strain on her neck, arms, and back as the infant is pulled away from her upper body. The infant or older baby may have discomfort in the neck which may result in premature cessation of the session. This can contribute to frustration in the baby and the baby may even drift to sleep, though unsatisfied. Then the mother may not fully empty the milk in her breast leading to painful engorgement or a diminished milk supply if the mother does not empty her breastmilk through feeding or expressing her milk with a pump or by hand. When mom is hurting, especially on her breast or nipple, she may offer the breast less and even substitute some formula. The lack of stimulation of the breast can lead to less milk production and further exasperate the condition.

As previously mentioned, engorgement can lead to a milk duct being clog, which is referred to as mastitis and requires medical attention. However, this complication is most likely avoided by frequent feedings or expressing of the breast milk. Through my research, I have discovered that many parents are misinformed about the frequency of feeding for breastfed infants who often feed every couple of hours. The feeding goal for breastfed infants is about 10-12 feedings every 24 hours versus the 6-8 feedings amongst formula fed babies. There is no magic number of feedings because each baby is different. It's more important to feed the baby as often as they give you feeding cues, which some people refer to as feeding on demand.

Another leading cause of breast or nipple pain happens when your baby becomes enamored with the sounds and visual cues of the outside world, and they turn their head in distraction with your nipple still in their mouth. Ouch! Of course, the most obvious but often unanticipated reason for pain is the emergence of your baby's teeth. In rare cases, a newborn is born with a tooth, or one erupts shortly after they are born. Sometimes dentist will remove those early teeth. At some point, all babies will develop teeth but that need not end your breastfeeding journey. You can learn to nurse around them.

Any of these preventable situations can cause great discomfort and, over time, can set off a snowball of problems that lead to premature ending of breastfeeding if not addressed. Paying attention to the way the baby is latched on, positioning, teeth development, as well as the frequency of feedings can help to alleviate the major sources of breast and nipple discomfort.

Refreshment

Maybe you too are experiencing pain and discomfort when you attempt to get your needs met. Is there something you are doing or refusing to do that may be contributing to your delay in receiving the vital resources you need to develop and thrive? Poor positioning, being distracted, and not opening your mouth widely enough for an ever present and loving God to fill it often result in undernourishment. First, position yourself closer to God leaving no room for anything to come between you. God promises in James 4:8 that if "you come near to God, he will come near to you."

Second, though it is easy to get distracted by the sights and sounds of the world which the Bible describes in I John 2:16 as "the lust of the flesh, the lust of the eyes, and the pride of life," keep your eyes fixed on the source of your provision. This means making pleasing God your focus. While it is hard to please your parents, your boss, your friends or your significant other because their requirements change daily, only one thing is needed to please God: Faith. How do we best demonstrate our faith in God? Roman 12: 1 says "Therefore, I urge you, brothers and sisters, in view of God's mercy, to offer your bodies as a living sacrifice, holy and pleasing to God—this is your true and proper worship." Let me translate. Just put your whole life in God's hands in the same way that your infant rest securely in your lap. As the kid's nursery rhyme says, "put your whole self in and shake it all about." Finally, tell God what you need and keep your mouth wide open, filled with praise, in anticipation of receiving all you need.

Please meditate on the following thought: Though pain may cause some mothers to discontinue their breastfeeding prematurely, God will never allow pain, even if it is inflicted by you, to interrupt the plan of care for you. No one has ever endured the level of pain God has endured in the parental relationship. God gave his first children, Adam and Eve, perfection in the form of paradise and they betrayed him by entertaining a strange serpent's accusation that God was not giving them all that they needed. Listening to the serpent, with its deceitful spirit, undermined Adam and Eve's trust in God. The deception caused them to believe that knowing good and evil would give them the ability to play God and make the best choices for themselves, which would lead to their satisfaction. They were wrong, of course. Adam and Eve's disobedience was ultimately a rejection of God's plan and resulted in them being overwhelmed after trying to decipher through all the information available to make the best choice for themselves. The responsibility for self-care was a burden that God never intended them to have. That was not the end of God's pain. When God finally had a perfectly obedient, loyal and loving son, Jesus, he had to sacrifice him to reconcile with all the rest of his children who were full of disobedience and contempt for him. Children like you and me. Despite the despicable act, the price of our full maturation as daughters of God was counted by Jesus as pure joy.

$\mathcal{D}ay$ 10

How Do I Know My Baby Has Received Enough Milk?

"Instead, I have calmed and quieted myself, like a weaned child who no longer cries for its mother's milk. Yes, like a weaned child is my soul within me. "- Psalm 131:2

Appetizer

Let's talk about how to end each feeding session with your child. This will help address one of the most frequently asked questions about breastfeeding. "How do I know my baby has received enough milk during a feeding session?"

During infancy, your baby may suddenly go into a deep sleep on your lap with milk dripping from the side of his or her mouth when they are satisfied. Once the baby reaches the toddler stage, they may gently release your boob and walk away to do something else. Yes, I did say they may be walking and breastfeeding, and if you imagined that means they have teeth also, your imagination is correct. My son, who breastfed for 2 years and 2 months, started trying to turn his head and watch TV with my nipple still in his mouth around 18 months. I quickly helped him understand this behavior would get him kicked off the boob. Immediately, he stopped doing that.

Entrée

Psalm 131 describes the ideal ending to both an individual session of breastfeeding and the overall process of breastfeeding with a specific child. In the short term, we would love for our child(ren) to appear calm at the end of each feeding. Just as you would put the fork down or pull away from the table after having finished a good meal, our children often do the same.

Although I have described the ideal ending to each feeding, other factors may cause the endings to be less than ideal. There are numerous distractions and interruptions including work, other family responsibilities, sleep, restroom breaks, etc. But despite these interruptions, babies usually demonstrate calm when they are satisfied with their feeding, unless there is an underlying illness or irritation like teething. When babies begin to teeth, they may want to breastfeed for comfort even if they are not hungry. For some reason babies are compelled to suck and that motion calms them, which is why pacifiers were created. Yet, your breast is even more soothing than a pacifier because it is attached to you. Your whole presence is a source of comfort.

As I mentioned in a previous chapter, the best indication that your baby is getting enough milk is wet or poopy diapers and weight gain. Like a well-watered garden grows, anything that is well nourished grows. If your baby is gaining weight appropriately, which will be assessed by a health care provider at your child's regular checkups, rest assured your baby is getting enough milk.

Refreshment

Mother, are you growing? Let me rephrase the question. Are you able to achieve steady progress toward your own goals surrounding physical, mental, spiritual, and emotional health? Do you have goals in these areas? If so, do you keep track of your progress? If you are not tracking, how will you know whether you are making progress? I encourage you to use the

Nurture for the Nurturer companion journal to keep up with your goals, but any journal will do. If you do not have any goals for your own physical, mental, spiritual and emotional health, would you consider making one. Afterall, God has a goal for you in these areas, and it is recorded in 3 John 1:2. "Dear friend, I pray that you may enjoy good health and that ALL may go well with you, even as your soul is getting along well."

Is your soul like a weaned child, satisfied with the nutrition you have received, or do you find yourself crying out or fussy because of hunger pains in your own soul? Do you spend time connecting with God long enough to really be refilled and refreshed, or are you just snacking? Like a toddler, have you become so distracted by noises or happenings in your environment that you stop attending to your own nourishment? What is getting in your way when you try to fill yourself with God's word and tender care? Can you write a list of those things and identify whether they are legitimate things that need your attention or if they are just noisy distractions?

How can you distinguish between a legitimate task and a noisy distraction? Legitimate tasks are things that you are actually responsible for and have the ability and resources to perform. Noisy distractions are typically things that you have no control over because you are NOT responsible for them. Or you may be responsible for the task, but you do not have the resources to take care of it at THIS time. These distractions often manifest in the form of commands that say "You should..." or "I should..." For example, think of the sentence "You should organize your drawers, clearly separating socks from underwear." Do you have drawer dividers? Do you have time to do that? If the answer is no AND your laundry is clean and folded, which is a miracle within itself, regardless if it is put away or not, then the suggestion is a distraction.

Here are two more "I should" or "You Should" commands that really tempt new moms who are eager to get back in shape, "I should've cooked instead of having fast food" or "I should be doing Peloton or Zumba." Is it bad to choose convenience sometimes? Do you own a Peloton? Do you have access to a Zumba instructor, or do you even like to dance for that matter? If the answer is no to those questions, then those suggestions are distractions. How can I say this when we all have been beat over the head with the importance of physical fitness? I'm a wellness coach, so trust me on this one. Physical fitness is absolutely important, but it should be reasonable and achievable, not a burden. Walking or lifting the car seat several times a day, which is almost 30 pounds once you add your baby to it, all count. Also, remember, if you are concerned about "getting your body back" specifically your stomach, or looking "snatched", breastfeeding is one of the best ways to achieve that goal because it helps to contract your uterus back to regular size, which is partly responsible for your belly bulge. Additionally, breastfeeding helps burn a few calories.

On a more serious note, maybe it is harder for you to classify the "I should" as a distraction because it is something extremely important like assisting with the health of a loved one or the need to earn extra income. Regarding income, is there an avenue available for you to earn more money that won't cost more money in the form of childcare? Or could you eliminate an unnecessary expense and save money? Regarding the sick loved one, maybe you think you should do something to prevent or cure their illness. If God has given you the wisdom, skill, resources, AND time to do so, go for it. Otherwise showing your support and care is good enough because your Google medical or nursing degree can result in more harm than good anyway. Take this from a professionally trained researcher, who knows the perils of Google.

Before I completed my doctoral training in public health, I once used a Google cure to help my mom with tooth pain and she had an allergic reaction that caused her lips to swell. In the end, she finally decided to go to the dentist, which is what she should have done in the first place. What should I have done? Just offer her a ride to the dentist. Now, after I completed my research training, there have been at least five or six instances when I have used my research skills to literally help guide medical staff to the right treatment plan for myself and my family. In three cases, it literally saved someone's life. One of those times, the life that needed saving was my own when I was rushed into an emergency C-section surgery to have my first child. So, I'm not assuming that you are not qualified to help, but instead of telling yourself "I should do this or that", ask yourself "Can I do that?" or "Do I have what I need to do that?" or "Is someone else better equipped and more available to do that than me?" These questions have freed up my time like nothing else has.

If the things grabbing your attention are legitimate, are you able to make a schedule for those things to get done so you are assured they will not go undone while you prioritize your own spiritual and emotional nourishment?

Also, I have lived long enough to know that you did not develop these extraordinary expectations of yourself on your own. Society pushes women to be bionic heroes as though we can achieve perfection, but it is a lie. Motherhood will expose your perfectionist tendencies like nothing else I have ever experienced. Use this time as an opportunity to break free from the unrealistic expectations you and others have placed on yourself. I challenge you. For one night do not do search and rescue in trying to find the stray Cheerio that may have fallen under a chair or car seat. If you do not have toddlers yet and can't relate to the Cheerio scenario, then just leave a dish in the sink overnight.

Also, how will you know you have received enough nourishment? Today's Bible passage suggests that the signs of soul satisfaction are an inner quietness and calm. Depending on what you are facing in your life, the amount of nurture and nourishment needed to achieve this inner calm and quiet may vary. Sometimes your nurturing session may last a while and other days it may be relatively short, like just 10-15 minutes. Yet one thing is certain, just as a child needs to eat every day, you will need daily nurturing. Create a plan to read or listen to the Bible. Try it out and make changes as you need to until you find a good schedule or pattern for yourself. In addition, you may experience nurture by listening to songs that remind you of God's promises and love.

Remember God's not just concerned about your spiritual health but your overall health as well. Your plan could include things that add to your emotional and physical health like grooming or surrounding yourself with things that evoke feelings of peace and pleasure. If you are confined, are you able to add beautiful images or peaceful music to your space? No matter what you choose to do, just invest in your own overall health daily.

Day 11

Breastfeeding During Times of Separation, NICU or Prison Included

"When she saw that he was a fine child, she hid him for three months. But when she could hide him no longer, she got a papyrus basket for him and coated it with tar and pitch. Then she placed the child in it and put it among the reeds along the bank of the Nile. His sister stood at a distance to see what would happen to him. Then Pharaoh's daughter went down to the Nile to bathe, and her attendants were walking along the riverbank. She saw the basket among the reeds and sent her female slave to get it. She opened it and saw the baby. He was crying, and she felt sorry for him. "This is one of the Hebrew babies," she said. Then his sister asked Pharaoh's daughter, "Shall I go and get one of the Hebrew women to nurse the baby for you?" "Yes, go," she answered. So, the girl went and got the baby's mother. Pharaoh's daughter said to her, "Take this baby and nurse him for me, and I will pay you." So, the woman took the baby and nursed him. When the child grew older, she took him to Pharaoh's daughter, and he became her son. She named him Moses, saying, "I drew him out of the water." -Exodus 2:2-10

Appetizer

Without knowing the context, this story may seem so irrelevant to our current cultural context and political landscape. Yet, it speaks to some of the most difficult circumstances a new mother can face, especially regarding breastfeeding, such as hazardous environments, threats of genocide, and early separation between a mother and baby. This story simultaneously illustrates the power of breastfeeding to prevent infant death and possibly delay mother-baby separation that could have long-term detrimental effects.

Moses, a Hebrew, was born as an ethnic minority in Egypt. At the time of his birth, the Pharaoh of Egypt was committing genocide by executing Hebrew male infants. If Moses' mother, Jochebed, had not engaged in the uncertain endeavor of sending him down the river, it was likely that her home would have been invaded by Egyptian officials and he would have been killed. This is the most extreme form of infant mortality.

What a risky move for a mother to place an infant into the hazardous environment of the Nile River, surely teeming with crocodiles, snakes, and potentially strong currents. Moses was only protected by a makeshift basket and a child chaperone following along from a distance to report on his fate. Desperate situations can lead to a mother making bold moves in effort to protect and sustain her child or children. While the situation, indeed, was desperate,

Jochebed must have been hopeful. How do I know? Hope is the opposite of dismay, which is a sudden sense of hopelessness accompanied by feelings of powerlessness. Dismay immobilizes, but hope can cause you to chart a way when none are visible.

Breastfeeding was Jochebed's strategy to save her son, Moses. The Princess of Egypt wanted to rescue Moses and since there was no commercially made infant formula, the only way for him to survive would be for someone to nurse him. Moses' sister, who watched from a distance as he was recovered from the river offered to find a nurse, who she knew would be her and Moses' mother. That quick suggestion seems to have been strategic. The successful plan was a blessing from the Lord in granting her precious time to be reunited with her son to instill her values in him and give him his foundational nurturing herself. It could be implied that she was able to keep Moses in her custody until he was weaned from breastfeeding, which may have been as old as the age of 4. Moses' chances of survival were exponentially multiplied, and Jochebed's grief over separation was delayed.

Entrée

In 2020, most of us cannot conceive of a situation like Jochebed's unless you are like one of the refugee mothers who sought asylum in the USA only to be forcefully separated from your newborn at an immigrant detention center, or you are in one of the jails or prisons that still practice mother-infant separation. While physical genocide is illegal, there still are policies in place that contribute to the economic and social displacement of families disproportionately impacting minorities and those who are economically poor. I have already mentioned policies regarding immigration and incarceration. But I will highlight a few others that impact mothers in less extreme circumstances and inhibit the success of their breastfeeding.

Today, many communities endure staggering rates of infant mortality, which is the death of a child before age 1. The risk factors are low birth weight and preterm birth, which are mostly caused by mom's exposure to a physically toxic or stressful environment. Discriminatory housing practices and poorer protection of lower wage workers results in minorities and people living in low-income neighborhoods being exposed to toxic chemicals such as lead, asbestos, allergens that cause asthma, toxic warehouse fumes, gases, water, and soil pollution.[7] Even if the mother is not directly exposed to a hazardous environment, her ancestor's exposure to toxic and stressful environments takes a few generations to overcome genetically.

Exposure to these agents contributes to reproductive harm that can cause second and third generations of women to have low birth weight or preterm delivery resulting in the baby staying in the

---

[7] Taylor, Larita Webb. The effects of traumatic stress on birth outcomes of African American and White women. The University of Memphis, 2014.

NICU after delivery, separating mom and baby. [8] However, premature babies need their mother's milk the most because their immature stomach and intestines cannot break down the proteins in cow milk.

If the above cases of infant-mother separation such as hospitalization, detention, or incarceration do not apply to you or anyone you know, here is one that most likely will: maternity leave. In the introduction, I described how only 16% of women in the USA have access to paid maternity leave, and how almost 1 out of every 4 mothers will return to work 10 days after having their baby, which greatly impacts how long they continue to breastfeed.

Though the policies may not be as extreme as killing a newborn, any policy or preventable circumstance that contributes to the premature separation of mothers can be distressing, but it does not have to mean the end of breastfeeding. Breastfeeding can still be a preemptive strategy to help overcome threats to your and your newborn's physical, social, and emotional health. Now, there are multiple options for mothers to express and safely store their milk including hand expression of their milk or using a manual or electric breast pump to store their milk for giving to the newborn later.

Many policies have changed to help accommodate breastfeeding mothers whether at home, in the

---

[8] Taylor, Larita Webb. The effects of traumatic stress on birth outcomes of African American and White women. The University of Memphis, 2014.

hospital, or even in prison. I would like to assume it is because we have more women policy makers. Hospitals are becoming more aware of the benefits of breastfeeding and will even provide a breast pump to mothers of premature babies or allow them to cup feed the baby the breastmilk, although the hospitals in lower income or minority areas still need to catch up to these practices which are referred to as "Baby Friendly."

In the United States, many states have passed laws requiring workplaces to provide safe and sanitary places (not a restroom) and extra breaks for mothers to pump or express her milk. Check in the appendix to see what laws your state has regarding breastfeeding. Also, some jails and prisons allow mothers to have contact time for the purpose of breastfeeding that otherwise would not be granted and some even allow the baby to stay with the mother. I have created a special appendix to address this policy.

Dessert

When Moses, from today's Bible verse, grew up, God appointed him to lead the children of Israel out of their years of oppression in Egypt. During the encounter recorded in Exodus 6:3, God introduced Moses to El Shaddai, the many breasted God, which implies God's all sufficiency, to assure Moses of who would be available to him during the journey. The passage states, "I appeared to Abraham, to Isaac and to Jacob as God Almighty (in Hebrew, "El Shaddai"), but by my name the LORD (in Hebrew, "Yahweh") I did not make myself fully known to them." As I mentioned in the meditation on Day 1, El Shaddai is most often translated from Hebrew into English as "God Almighty". While that is a valid translation, it loses some of the implications, especially now that we understand how powerful the breast really is.

Just as Moses' own mother, Jochebed, cast him upon the water to save his life from the Egyptians and, after he was rescued, helped him to thrive by nursing him at her breast, God, El Shaddai (the breasted one), would lead Moses as the Israelites escaped the wrath of Pharaoh by passing through the waters of the Red Sea. Furthermore, El Shaddai would be there to sustain them when they reached the other side and entered a seemingly resource-deprived wilderness.

It was like God saying to Moses, "if I brought you through the waters safely in a reed basket, surely I can bring the whole group of Israelites through the water. Just like your mother nourished you to health, I will nourish and sustain all of you. In fact, I have spared and preserved your life, Moses, for this very purpose." This reminds me of a song performed by Chaka Khan and the late great Whitney Houston called "I'm Every Woman." The song glorifies a woman's ability to meet a variety of needs naturally and encourages a person to seek her out for this purpose. We could change the lyrics to "I'm El Shaddai. It's all in me. Anything you need done baby I'll do it masterfully." While women cannot do everything because there is a place for both men and women in the world, the amazing things we can do are because all of us are created in the image of God, El Shaddai.

Did you catch that? Mother, you are created in the image of God. All within yourself, in your breast, is the nourishment that your newborn needs. Even in a famine or drought your body will still supply breastmilk for the infant and research studies have confirmed that. People talk about a figurative "Mother Nature", almost like a replacement for God, but I think "Mother Nurture" is a real God-created and God-ordained force to be reckoned with.

Refreshment

Is there any area of your life where you feel like you are barely keeping your head above the water and are at risk of drowning? Do you feel like you need to be rescued from a toxic relationship, job, living environment or even imprisonment or detention? While God often uses other people to help meet our needs, there are times that God alone will work miraculous deliverance in our lives so that we learn to put our faith in God. Just like the Princess of Egypt probably heard Moses crying in the river, God will respond to your cry. As you hold a fraction of the power of God to sustain life within your very breast, God or El Shaddai, the breasted one, holds ALL power housed within the trinity (God the Father, the Son, and the Holy Spirit) to sustain your every need and will forcefully deliver and protect you at a moment's notice, if needed.

Just like all the immoral leaders and lawmakers we have referred to today can use their power to oppress and even annihilate people groups, the enemy of your soul wants to annihilate you through all forms of bondage and oppression literally trying to take you under and overcome you. The devil will hold you hostage, but God loves you so much that he gave Jesus as a ransom for your life. Jesus' life, death, and resurrection was enough to recover any and everyone who needs to be recovered out of the enemy's flood waters. The Bible says, "Everyone who calls on the name of the Lord will be saved."- Romans 10:13

This verse in Roman's was originally written in Greek and that word for Lord was "kurio", the person with absolute ownership rights and in this case, your creator. Just as Jochebed was able to be reunited with her baby and nurse him, God cannot wait to draw you out of the flood waters and pull you close to comfort and nurture you. Remember, this is basically what Jesus said before giving his life as a ransom: "How often I have longed to gather your children together, as a hen gathers her chicks under her wings", Matthew 23:37. Hens hide their chicks when an enemy is looking for them or when a strong storm is raging. Will you let God pull you up and out of the challenge you are facing, while providing your every need? Just call out to your creator and you too will be rescued.

𝒟ay 12

How Will I Know When to Wean My Child or Stop Breastfeeding?

"When her husband Elkanah went up with all his family to offer the annual sacrifice to the LORD and to fulfill his vow, Hannah did not go. She said to her husband, "After the boy is weaned, I will take him and present him before the LORD, and he will live there always." "Do what seems best to you," her husband Elkanah told her. "Stay here until you have weaned him; only may the LORD make good his word." So, the woman stayed at home and nursed her son until she had weaned him. After he was weaned, she took the boy with her, young as he was, along with a three-year-old bull, an ephah of flour and a skin of wine, and brought him to the house of the LORD at Shiloh. "I prayed for this child, and the LORD has granted me what I asked of him. So now I give him to the LORD. For his whole life he will be given over to the LORD." And he worshiped the LORD there." - I Samuel 1: 22- 27

Appetizer

Why are we talking about weaning, the ending of breastfeeding, when you are just starting or in some cases restarting your breastfeeding journey? Have you ever heard the phrase "begin with the end in mind"? Well today, we are going to do just that; paint a vision of the goals you intend achieve through breastfeeding to motivate you throughout your journey. In today's Bible passage, we see Hannah had a vision for her breastfeeding. She intended to nurse, another word for breastfeed, until she could dedicate her son Samuel in service to the Lord, who is the ultimate nurturer.

In this passage, we see a woman who had struggled to conceive a child afterwards fulfill a public vow to breastfeed her son for a specified time. A vow is another way to describe a commitment or promise. In our modern context, we are most familiar with vows declared in a formal marriage ceremony. Nevertheless, Hannah vowed to her husband and ultimately to God to nurture the child God provided in her grief by breastfeeding him until he was developed enough for her to leave him with the priest for her son to begin his lifelong specific service to the Lord. Samuel may have been 3 years old when he was weaned. Hannah publicized her vow and it brought support from her husband and community. This same principle can work for you.

Entrée

At the beginning of this devotional, I described the importance of making a commitment to your breastfeeding journey as a critical step in healthy and beneficial breastfeeding success. In parenting, we make many vows, though most are unspoken. We make vows not to repeat mistakes we have witnessed other parents make or we vow to do things we believe will have a lasting positive impact on our child. These kinds of private vows are good to make, but a public vow is even better because it invites others to help you remain accountable to your goal.

What goals do you hope to achieve by breastfeeding? First, try to determine what breastfeeding goal will work for you and your family. Second, consider creating a breastfeeding vow? Identify with whom you can share these goals so that you will be held accountable. Finally, try your best to not let anything get in the way of your fulfilling your vow. The support person or people you identify should be people you can trust to help you fulfill this vow when things get challenging.

You might wonder what is considered a reasonable breastfeeding timeframe. As I mentioned earlier, United States national guidelines recommend breastfeeding exclusively, with no other food or drinks, until 6 months of age and breastfeeding with other complimentary foods until at least the child becomes 1 year old. The World Health Organization recommends 2 years of breastfeeding. These recommendations are based on the developmental needs of the baby and the long-term benefits of breastfeeding, ranging from improved cognitive ability and social attachments to chronic disease prevention.

As I have described throughout this devotional, there will be challenges, some expected and some unexpected, but I pray you are able to navigate. You may be surprised that you may breastfeed longer than expected once you get into the swing of things. Also, your precious baby may have other plans as well, which could include premature weaning or refusing to let go of the boobs at your appointed deadline.

Dessert

Considering this is our last day together, why not have a little dessert: My own personal weaning stories, which I hope will inspire you to dream of your happy ending.

I had initially decided to breastfeed my firstborn at least a year no matter what. Two unexpected things happened. Around the time my daughter, turned 8 months old, I discovered that she had about 14 food allergies. Most of the things to which she was allergic had been discovered through only her exposure to my breastmilk. These allergies caused severe eczema and what we had mistook for "colic" from her hollering throughout the night due to her tummy ache. By the grace of God and through the process of elimination, I figured out nine of her food allergies prior to a consultation with an allergy doctor, with cow's milk being the main culprit. Upon this discovery, I could not switch her to cow's milk, soy milk, or goat's milk even if I wanted to do so when she turned 1. It was safer for me to breastfeed, however, it caused me to have a very restricted diet. There was no garlic which eliminated Italian food. She was allergic to dairy, beef, eggs, wheat, fish, shellfish, tree nuts, peanuts, and citrus fruits. The plus side was that I lost a significant amount of weight. I was 8 pounds lighter after breastfeeding than I was prior to my pregnancy.

I told you there were two unexpected things that shaped my decision to wean my daughter, and the first was the allergies. Then, about a month after my daughter's 1st birthday, we discovered that we were pregnant with my son. We had not been trying to conceive and I, jokingly but seriously, asked my Gynecologist where the baby came from. I had not bought into the myth that breastfeeding prevented pregnancy, though it had delayed my period until 7 months postpartum. Yet, you will understand when you have a busy schedule and a toddler running around, that there is barely any time to be intimate. In this case, I legitimately could not remember the last time my husband and I had been intimate.

I knew I would breastfeed the new baby, and in case he had food allergies like my daughter, I would need a break from the strict diet. So, at 16 months, I forced my daughter to wean. Momma needed freedom for those last 6 months of pregnancy. I am at high risk for a miscarriage during pregnancy because of my history of blood clots, so I was required take Heparin injections every day throughout each pregnancy until I delivered. I never even considered how the Heparin would affect my breastmilk. I primarily thought about needing a piece of cake, lemonade, and a cheese puff. Since completing my lactation training, I now know that Heparin or Lovenox would not have harmed my daughter even if had I continued to breastfeed her.

With my second born, I knew I would give him at least as much time to breastfeed as I gave my daughter, but he had other plans. My husband, who had been amazingly supportive of my decision to breastfeed both children, inquired about how long was I going to keep breastfeeding this "big boy". After my son was over one year old, I told my husband I would quit once he turned two. As an aside, my husband wanted the enlarged breasts back, so he was eagerly waiting for my son's birthday to arrive. The second birthday came, and my son was not understanding the disappearance of the boobs. By this time, my husband had started school full-time alongside his full-time job, which took him out of the house from 7:30 AM until midnight. After a day's struggle to distract my son, at night I gave in to our nighttime bonding ritual and nursed him. About a month later my husband discovered that I had been sneaking to feed my son.

It sounds silly now, the concept of sneaking to nurse. Yet, I know there are more people who secretly breastfeed out there. I will warn you, many people who were previously supportive of you breastfeeding, jump off the fan wagon after the baby can walk and talk. At this point, the breastfeeding shamers become very vocal. You learn to ignore them or just keep it a secret like I did to some extent. You should not have to be secretive, just tell others to mind their own lunch.

Let me get back to the story. I always had the privilege of working from home since before my daughter was born, so I rarely ever pumped my milk because the kids were always around me except when I traveled out of town for work. Not long after my son turned 2 years old, I had a 4-day work trip. I committed the error of all breastfeeding mommy errors by forgetting to pack my breast pump.

Under normal circumstances, this would be a reason to completely flip out. I remained calm and figured that since my son was mostly nursing at night, that I would not need to express much milk. I found a cup in the hotel and hand expressed. Not very much breast milk came out the first day. I was scared that I would get painfully engorged by day two, but, thankfully, I did not. Even more, I only expressed my milk once that day. The third day there was no engorgement and almost nothing came out. By the time my trip was over, I was assured that the interruption had done for me what I did not have the strength to do myself, and that was end my breastfeeding journey with my son by drying up my milk. Girl was I wrong!

The night after returning home, my son begged to latch, and I let him try. I was convinced nothing would come out and the previous night nursing's had been total comfort feedings. So, midway through his attempt to nurse I snatched my boob out while exclaiming, "Will, there's nothing in there you need to stop!" Believe it or not, there were droplets of milk. A child's ability to draw out milk by latching on to the breast is more powerful than any other tool! With the milk flowing again, I continued breastfeeding a little longer. Two months after my son's 2nd birthday, we made a pact, and he finally gave up the boobs.

Refreshment

Today, first, you get to be creative. In the space provided on the next page, draw a picture that represents the benefits that you and your baby may experience because of your choice to breastfeed. You may even write single words or phrases like, "smart" or draw a picture of a happy child. There is no limit on what you draw or how far into the future you set your view. For example, I knew breastfeeding would help my stomach get back to my pre-pregnancy size faster and would decrease the chances of my children ever struggling with obesity or diabetes. So, I may have drawn a picture of my daughter and my son with big brains, big smiles, and trim bodies while holding briefcases as young adults. I, literally, thought that far ahead. Feel free to use your own paper or canvas, because I do not know how big your imagination is. Second, you can share your vision with the same support person you identified earlier, who you believe will hold you accountable when challenges arise. Finally, determine how you will celebrate yourself once you fulfill your vow. Remember, this guide is all about remembering to nurture the nurturer.

Mommy Benefits

Child Benefits

Conclusion

I have been delighted to serve as your "cheerleader, coach, and companion" throughout this phase of your breastfeeding journey. I hope you are encouraged to overcome some of the most common breastfeeding challenges. As this book outlines, one of the most difficult and often neglected challenges for mothers, regardless of their breastfeeding status, is self-care. I hope you have developed a level of mindfulness and appreciation for your own needs, as well as strategies to address those needs. It has been my greatest joy to introduce or reintroduce you, to a faithful companion and guide, who can accompany you on the rest of your journey: El Shaddai. Finally, this book has only touched the surface of the challenges that may occur during breastfeeding. I pray that you will find the additional support that you need from the various organizations and resources listed in the appendices.

Appendix 1. Federal Policy on Breastfeeding

You have the right to breastfeed your baby almost anywhere, including public places, work, and even in some jails and prisons. Breastfeeding may even excuse you from jury duty.

Federal Legislation

The Affordable Care Act (ACA) 2010, often called Obamacare, amended Section 4207 of the Fair Labor Standards Act (FLSA) of 1938 (29 U.S. Code 207) requiring an employer to provide reasonable break time for an employee to express breast milk for her nursing child up to one year after the child's birth whenever the employee has a need. The employer is not required to pay the employee if these breaks occur outside of the employees break time, but the employer must provide a place, other than a bathroom, for the employee to express breast milk. Some employers with less than 50 employees are not subject to the regulations if they impose "undue hardships" on the employer. However, the federal law does not stop a state from making laws the provides more requirements of employers.

Also, the ACA, requires new private health insurance plans, and all the plans on the health insurance marketplace, to provide coverage for breastfeeding support, supplies i.e., breast pumps, and lactation counseling at no cost to the person insured.

Appendix 2. State Breastfeeding Laws in the USA

In this appendix, I have included a brief overview of the policy landscape on breastfeeding in each of the 50 U.S. states and territories. Look up the laws governing your state using this list, which is reproduced from the National Conference of State Legislatures and StateNet. Please check their website listed in the appendix for any updates to these laws since the end of 2020.

Alabama

Ala. Code § 22-1-13 (2006) allows a mother to breastfeed her child in any public or private location.

Alaska

Alaska Stat. § 29.25.080 and § 01.10.060 (1998) prohibit a municipality from enacting an ordinance that prohibits or restricts a woman breastfeeding a child in a public or private location where the woman and child are otherwise authorized to be. The law clarifies that lewd conduct, lewd touching, immoral conduct, indecent conduct, and similar terms do not include the act of a woman breastfeeding a child in a public or private location where the woman and child are otherwise authorized to be.

2014 Alaska House Concurrent Resolution 18 (2014) encourages hospitals and birthing facilities in the state to participate in the Baby-Friendly Hospital Initiative and to support breastfeeding.

Arizona

Ariz. Rev. Stat. Ann § 13-1402 (2006) specifies that indecent exposure does not include an act of breastfeeding by a mother.

Ariz. Rev. Stat. Ann § 41-1443 (2006) entitles a mother to breastfeed in any public place or place of public accommodation where the mother is otherwise lawfully present.

Arkansas

Ark. Stat. Ann. § 20-27-2001(2007) states that a woman may breastfeed a child in a public place or any place where other individuals are present.

Ark. Stat. Ann. § 5-14-112 (2007) defines indecent exposure and specifies that a woman is not committing indecent exposure for breastfeeding a child in a public place or any place where other individuals are present.

Ark. Stat. Ann. § 11-5-116 (2009) requires an employer to provide reasonable unpaid break time each day to an employee who needs to express breast milk for her child and requires an employer to make a reasonable effort to provide a private, secure and sanitary room or other location other than a toilet stall where an employee can express her breast milk.

Ark. Stat. Ann. § 20-56-305 (2019) requires at least one of three statements to advertise medical marijuana, one of which warns about the potential harms to an unborn child or child following marijuana use during pregnancy or breastfeeding (SB 441).

California

Cal. Government Code § 12920-12923 (1980) and § 12926 (2012) make it unlawful to engage in specified discriminatory practices on the basis of sex, which includes breastfeeding or medical conditions related to breastfeeding, in the opportunity to seek, obtain and hold employment or housing.

Cal. Civil Code § 43.3 (1997) allows a mother to breastfeed her child in any location, public or private, except the private home or residence of another, where the mother and the child are otherwise authorized to be present. Cal. Welfare and Institutions Code § 11218 (2013) specifies an applicant or recipient of aid is entitled to breastfeed her child in a county welfare department or other county office.

Cal. Health and Safety Code § 1647 (1999) declares that the procurement, processing, distribution or use of human milk for the purpose of human consumption is considered to be a rendition of a service rather than a sale of human milk.

Cal. Code of Civil Procedure § 210.5 (2000) requires the Judicial Court to adopt a standardized jury summons for use, which must include a specific reference to the rules for breastfeeding mothers. AB 1814 (2000) created the law and directs the Judicial Council to adopt a rule of court to allow the mother of a breastfed child to postpone jury duty for a period of up to one year and that after one year, jury duty may be further postponed upon written request by the mother.

Cal. Labor Code § 1030 et seq. (2001) provides that employers need to allow a break and provide a room for a mother who desires to express milk in private. AB 1976 (2018) requires an employer to make reasonable efforts to provide an employee with the use of a room or a location other than a bathroom, for these purposes. SB 142 (2019) requires the room or location other than a bathroom to have prescribed features. Features an employer, among other things, to provide access to a sink and refrigerator in close proximity to the employee's workspace.

Cal. Health and Safety Code § 1648 (2006) requires a hospital that collects, processes, stores or distributes human milk collection from a mother exclusively for her own child to comply with the standards for collection, processing, storage or distribution of human milk by the Human Milk Banking Association of North America unless the department of health approves alternate standards. No screening tests are required to be performed on human milk collected from a mother exclusively for her own child.

Cal. Health and Safety Code § 123360 (2007) requires the Department of Public Health to include the promotion of mothers breastfeeding their infants in its public service campaign; and require the department to develop a model eight-hour training course and to promote exclusive breastfeeding and specify hospital staff for whom the training is appropriate.

Cal. Health and Safety Code § 1257.9 (2007) states the Department of Public Health shall recommend a minimum eight-hour training to appropriate staff in general acute care hospitals that provide maternity care and have exclusive patient breastfeeding rates in the lowest 25 percent of the state.

Cal. Government Code § 12926 (2012) states it is unlawful to engage in specified discriminatory practices in employment or housing accommodations on the basis of sex. The law provides that, for purposes of the act, the term sex also includes breastfeeding or medical conditions related to breastfeeding.

Cal. Health and Safety Code § 123367 (2013) requires all acute care and special hospitals that have a perinatal unit to adopt the "Ten Steps to Successful Breastfeeding" of the Baby-Friendly Hospital Initiative, or an evidence-based alternative with targeted outcomes adopted by a health care service plan, or the Model Hospital Policy Recommendations as defined by § 123366.

Cal. Education Code § 222 (2015) requires schools operated by a school district or a county office of education, the California School for the Deaf, the California School for the Blind, and charter schools to provide reasonable accommodations to a lactating pupil on a high school campus to express breast milk, breastfeed an infant child, or address other needs related to breastfeeding.

Cal. Penal Code § 4002.5 (2018) requires a County Sheriff, or the Administrator of a county jail, to develop and implement an infant and toddler breast milk feeding policy for lactating inmates detained or sentenced to a county jail that is based on accepted best practices (AB 2507).

Cal. Ed Code § 66271.9 (2018) requires the Community Colleges and the State University, and encourages satellite campuses, to provide reasonable accommodations to a lactating student to express breast milk, breast feed an infant child, or address other needs related to breastfeeding. Requires educational institutions to provide a sink in the new construction, replacement, expansion or renovation, in addition to access to a private and secure room for breastfeeding students (AB 2785).

Cal. Public Utilities Code § 99176 (2019) requires multimodal transit stations that begin construction or a renovation on or after January 1, 2021, to include a lactation room (AB 752).

Colorado

Colo. Rev. Stat. § 25-6-301 (2004) recognizes the benefits of breastfeeding and encourages mothers to breastfeed.

Colo. Rev. Stat. § 25-6-302 (2004) allows a mother to breastfeed in any place she has a right to be.

Colo. Rev. Stat. § 8-13.5-102 and § 8-13.5-104 (2008) acknowledge the benefits of breastfeeding and require an employer to provide reasonable break time for an employee to express breast milk for her nursing child for up to two years after the child's birth. The employer must make reasonable efforts to provide a place, other than a toilet stall, for the employee to express breast milk in privacy. The law also requires the Department of Labor and Employment to provide, on its website, information and links to other websites where employers can access information regarding methods to accommodate nursing mothers in the workplace.

Colo. Rev. Stat. § 13-71-119.5 (2015) provides a temporary excuse for a person who is breastfeeding from service as a juror.

CO SB 224 (2019) allows the state agency in charge of licensing cannabis dispensaries to seek the assistance of the department of public health and environment on a range of issues, including the design of a warning sign for pregnant and breastfeeding women on the risks of using cannabis.

Connecticut

Conn. Gen. Stat. § 46a-64 (1997) prohibits places of public accommodation, resort or amusement from restricting or limiting the right of a mother to breastfeed her child.

Conn. Gen. Stat. Ann. § 53-34b (1997) provides that no person may restrict or limit the right of a mother to breastfeed her child.

Conn. Gen. Stat. § 31-40w (2001) requires employers to provide a reasonable amount of time each day to an employee who needs to express breast milk for her infant child and to provide accommodations where an employee can express her milk in private.

Conn. Gen. Stat § 51-217b (2012) states the Judicial Branch will maintain a website providing prospective jurors with general information regarding jury service, including information for breastfeeding women regarding their ability to postpone jury service. The website will provide information for Jury Administration in the event a breastfeeding woman would like to request a reasonable accommodation.

CT SB 13 (2018) requires the Department of Correction to establish prenatal, labor and postpartum services and supports, including a lactation policy, to women incarcerated at the York Correctional Institution.

CT HB 5210 (2018) requires individual insurance policies to cover breastfeeding support and counseling for any pregnant or breastfeeding woman and breastfeeding supplies, including but not limited to, a breast pump for any breastfeeding woman.

Public Act 19-48 (2019) provides Medicaid reimbursement for donor breast milk deemed medically necessary. (HB 7165)

Delaware

Del. Code Ann. tit. 31 § 310 (1997) entitles a mother to breastfeed her child in any location of a place of public accommodation wherein the mother is otherwise permitted.

District of Columbia

D.C. Code Ann. § 2-1402.81 et seq. (2007) amend the Human Rights Act of 1977 to include breastfeeding as part of the definition of discrimination on the basis of sex, to ensure a woman's right to breastfeed her child in any location, public or private, where she has the right to be with her child. The law provides that breastfeeding is not a violation of indecent exposure laws. The law also specifies that an employer shall provide reasonable daily unpaid break periods, as required by the employee, so that the employee may express breast milk for her child. These break periods shall run concurrently with any break periods that may already be provided to the employee. Requires that an employer make reasonable efforts to provide a sanitary room or other location, other than a bathroom or toilet stall, where an employee can express her breast milk in privacy and security. The location may include a childcare facility in close proximity to the employee's work location.

D.C. Law 22-179 (2018) requires the Deputy Mayor for Health and Human Services to expand and coordinate health care for infants and toddlers under age three, including increasing the utilization of breastfeeding among new mothers and strengthening the existing lactation support infrastructure.

Florida

Fla. Stat. § 383.015 (1993) allows a mother to breastfeed in any public or private location.

Fla. Stat. § 383.016 (1994) authorizes a facility lawfully providing maternity services or newborn infant care to use the designation "baby-friendly" on its promotional materials. The facility must be in compliance with at least eighty percent of the requirements developed by the Department of Health in accordance with UNICEF and World Health Organization baby-friendly hospital initiatives.

Fla. Stat. § 800 (1993), § 827.071 (2001) and Fla. Stat. § 847.0135 (2001) exclude breastfeeding from various sexual offenses, such as lewdness, indecent exposure and sexual conduct.

Georgia

Ga. Code § 31-1-9 (1999) states that the breastfeeding of a baby is an important and basic act of nurture which should be encouraged in the interests of maternal and child health and allows a mother to breastfeed her baby in any location where the mother and baby are otherwise authorized to be.

Ga. Code § 34-1-6 (1999) allows employers to provide daily unpaid break time for a mother to express breast milk for her infant child. Employers are also required to make a reasonable effort to provide a private location, other than a toilet stall, in close proximity to the workplace for this activity. The employer is not required to provide break time if to do so would unduly disrupt the workplace operations.

Hawaii

Hawaii Rev. Stat. § 367-3 (1999) requires the Hawaii Civil Rights Commission to collect, assemble and publish data concerning instances of discrimination involving breastfeeding or expressing breast milk in the workplace. The law prohibits employers to forbid an employee from expressing breast milk during any meal period or other break period.

Hawaii Rev. Stat. § 378-2 (2000) provides that it is unlawful discriminatory practice for any employer or labor organization to refuse to hire or employ, bar or discharge from employment, withhold pay from, demote or penalize a lactating employee because an employee breastfeeds or expresses milk at the workplace.

Hawaii Rev. Stat. § 489.21 and § 489-22 (2000) provide that it is a discriminatory practice to deny, or attempt to deny, the full and equal enjoyment of the goods, services, facilities, privileges, advantages, and accommodation of a place of public accommodations to a woman because she is breastfeeding a child. The law allows a private cause of action for any person who is injured by a discriminatory practice under this act.

House Concurrent Resolution 158 (2010) urges the Department of Human Services and the Department of Health to develop a program to encourage breastfeeding among mothers who receive assistance from Medicaid.

Hawaii Sess. Laws. Act. 249 (2013) requires specified employers to provide reasonable break time for an employee to express milk for a nursing child in a location, other than a bathroom, that is sanitary, shielded from view and free from intrusion. The law also requires employers to post notice of the application of this law in a conspicuous place accessible to employees.

Idaho

Idaho Code § 2-212 (2002) provides that a person who is not disqualified for jury service under § 2-209 may have jury service postponed by the court or the jury commissioner only upon a showing of undue hardship, extreme inconvenience, or public necessity, or upon a showing that the juror is a mother breastfeeding her child.

Idaho Code § 18-4101 (2018) revises provisions relating to breastfeeding; provides an exemption from indecent exposure and obscenity for the breastfeeding of a child.

Illinois

Ill. Rev. Stat. ch. 720 § 5/11-9 (1995) clarifies that breastfeeding of infants is not an act of public indecency.

Ill. Rev. Stat. ch. 20 § 2310/442 (1997) allows the Department of Public Health to conduct an information campaign for the general public to promote breastfeeding of infants by their mothers. The law allows the department to include the information in a brochure for free distribution to the general public.

Ill. Rev. Stat. Ch. 820 § 260 (2001) creates the Nursing Mothers in the Workplace Act. Requires that employers provide reasonable unpaid break time each day to employees who need to express breast milk. The law also requires employers to make reasonable efforts to provide a room or other location, other than a toilet stall, where an employee can express her milk in privacy. IL HB 1595 (2018) prohibits employers from reducing an employee's compensation for time used to express milk or to nurse a baby.

Ill. Rev. Stat. Ch. 740 § 137 (2004) creates the Right to Breastfeed Act. The law provides that a mother may breastfeed her baby in any location, public or private, where the mother is otherwise authorized to be; a mother who breastfeeds in a place of worship shall follow the appropriate norms within that place of worship.

Ill. Rev. Stat. Ch. 705 § 305/10.3 (2005) amends the Jury Act; provides that any mother nursing her child shall, upon her request, be excused from jury duty.

Ill. Senate Resolution 170 (2011) recognizes the unique health, economic, and societal benefits that breastfeeding provides to babies, mothers, families and the community and resolves the state of Illinois to work to ensure that barriers to initiation and continuation of breastfeeding are removed and that a women's right to breastfeed is upheld.

Ill. House Resolution 778 (2012) urges departments that assist families and children to offer and promote educational materials about breastfeeding.

Ill. Laws, P.A. 97-713 (2012) establishes the hospital infant feeding act and requires that every hospital that provides birthing services to adopt an infant feeding policy that promotes breastfeeding. The hospital must routinely communicate this policy to staff and authorizes the posting of the policy on the hospital's website.

Ill. Laws Public Act 99-228 (2015) creates the Lactation Accommodation in Airports Act and requires that airport managers to provide a room or other location space at each airport terminal behind the airport security screening area for members of the public to express breast milk in private.

Ill. Rev. Stat. Ch. 105 § 5/10-20.60, § 5/34-18.53 and 5/27A-5 (2017) require a public school, including a charter school, to provide reasonable accommodations to a lactating pupil on a school campus to express breast milk, breastfeed an infant child, or address other needs related to breastfeeding; provides for grievance procedures.

Ill. Rev. Stat. Ch. 68 § 5/2-102 (2017) states that "reasonable accommodations" means reasonable modifications or adjustments to the job application process or work environment that enable an applicant or employee affected by pregnancy, childbirth, or medical or common conditions related to pregnancy or childbirth to be considered for the position the applicant desires or to perform the essential functions of that position.

Ill. Rev. Stat. Ch. 25 § 130/8A-21 (2018) directs the Architect of the Capitol to designate at least one mother's lactation and wellness room in the State Capitol Building, the Howlett Building and the Stratton Building (HB 1042).

Ill. Rev. Stat. Ch. 55 § 5/5-1106 (2018) provides that on or before June 1, 2019, every facility that houses a circuit court room shall include at least one lactation room or area for members of the public to express breast milk in private that is located outside the confines of a restroom and includes, at minimum, a chair, a table, and an electrical outlet, as well as a sink with running water where possible (IL SB 3503).

Ill. Rev. Stat. Ch. 410 § 50/3.4 (2019) establishes a comprehensive list of a woman's rights with regard to pregnancy and childbirth, including the right to information on breastfeeding (IL HB 2).

Ill. Rev. Stat. Ch. 730 § 5/5-5-3.1 (2019) amends the Unified Code of Corrections, expands the factors accorded weight in favor of withholding or minimizing a sentence of imprisonment to include whether the defendant is the parent of a child or infant whose wellbeing will be negatively affected by the parent's absence, including if the child is breastfeeding (HB 2444).

IL HB 3509 (2019) amends the State Employees Group Insurance Act, the Insurance Code, and the Public Aid Code, provides that donated breast milk must be prescribed by a licensed medical practitioner, provides that milk must be obtained from a human milk bank that meets quality guidelines establishes by the Human Milk Banking Association of North America or is licensed by the Department of Public Health, removes a requirement that the infant must be critically ill.

Indiana

Ind. Code § 16-35-6 (2003) allows a woman to breastfeed her child anywhere the law allows her to be.

Ind. Code § 5-10-6-2 and § 22-2-14-2 (2008) provide that state and political subdivisions shall provide for reasonable paid breaks for an employee to express breast milk for her infant, make reasonable efforts to provide a room or other location, other than a toilet stall, where the employee can express breast milk in private and make reasonable efforts to provide for a refrigerator to keep breast milk that has been expressed. The law also provides that employers with more than 25 employees must provide a private location, other than a toilet stall, where an employee can express the employee's breast milk in private and if possible, to provide a refrigerator for storing breast milk that has been expressed.

Iowa

Iowa Code § 607A.5 (1994) allows a woman to be excused from jury service if she submits written documentation verifying, to the court's satisfaction, that she is the mother of a breastfed child and is responsible for the daily care of the child.

Iowa Code § 135.30A (2006) a woman may breastfeed the woman's own child in any public place where the woman's presence is otherwise authorized.

Kansas

Kan. Stat. Ann. § 43-158 (2006) allows a mother breastfeeding her child to be excused from jury service and allows jury service to be postponed until the mother is no longer breastfeeding the child.

Kan. Stat. Ann. § 65-1,248 (2006) provides that it is the public policy of Kansas that a mother's choice to breastfeed should be supported and encouraged to the greatest extent possible and that a mother may breastfeed in any place she has a right to be.

Kentucky

Ky. Rev. Stat. § 211-755 (2006) permits a mother to breastfeed her baby or express breast milk in any public or private location. Requires that breastfeeding may not be considered an act of public indecency, indecent exposure, sexual conduct, lewd touching or obscenity. Prohibits a municipality from enacting an ordinance that prohibits or restricts breastfeeding in a public or private place.

Ky. Rev. Stat. § 29A.100 (2007) directs judges at all levels of the court to excuse women who are breastfeeding or expressing breast milk from jury service until the child is no longer nursing.

Ky. Rev. Stat. § 344.040 (2019) makes it unlawful for an employer to fail to make reasonable accommodations for an employee with limitations related to pregnancy, childbirth, or a related condition, including but not limited to the need to express breastmilk (SB 18).

Louisiana

La. Rev. Stat. Ann. § 51.2247.1 (2001) prohibits discriminatory practices against and states that a mother may breastfeed her baby in any location, public or private, where the mother is otherwise authorized to be. Breastfeeding shall not be deemed an obscenity or be a violation of any other provision of law.

La. Rev. Stat. § 49:148.4.1 (2011) requires state-owned buildings to provide suitable accommodation for breastfeeding and lactation.

La. Rev. Stat. § 47:305.67 (2011) provides that the state sales and use tax shall not apply to the consumer purchase of breastfeeding items, including breast pumps and accessories, replacement parts, storage bags and accessories, and nursing bras.

La. Rev. Stat. Ann. § 46.1407 (2013) prohibits any child-placing agency, maternity home or residential home from discriminating against breastfed babies.

La. Rev. Stat. Ann. § 17:81 (2013) requires public school boards to adopt a policy to require each school to provide an appropriate, private room, other than a restroom, that may be used by an employee to express breast milk. The school must also provide a reasonable amount of break time to accommodate an employee needing to express breast milk for up to one year following the birth of her child.

La. Rev. Stat. Ann. § 17:407 (2014) prohibits any childcare facility from discriminating against breastfed babies.

Maine

Me. Rev. Stat. Ann. tit. 5, § 4634 (2001) amends the Maine Human Rights Act to declare that a mother has the right to breastfeed her baby in any location, whether public or private, as long as she is otherwise authorized to be in that location.

Me. Rev. Stat. Ann. tit. 26, § 604 (2009) requires an employer to provide adequate unpaid or paid break time to express breast milk for up to 3 years following childbirth. The employer must make reasonable efforts to provide a clean place, other than a bathroom, where an employee may express breast milk in privacy. The employer may not discriminate against an employee who chooses to express breast milk in the workplace.

ME HB 487 (2019) provides that it is unlawful employment discrimination for an employer to fail to provide a reasonable accommodation for an employee's pregnancy-related condition, including lactation, unless provision of an accommodation would impose an undue hardship on the employer.

Maryland

Md. Tax-General Code Ann. §11-211 (2001) exempts the sale of tangible personal property that is manufactured for the purpose of initiating, supporting or sustaining breastfeeding from the sales and use tax.

Md. Health-General Code Ann. § 20-801 (2003) permits a woman to breastfeed her infant in any public or private place and prohibits anyone from restricting or limiting this right.

Md. Education Code Ann. § 9.5-404 (2014) relates to the licensing and operation of childcare centers. The law requires childcare centers to promote proper nutrition and developmentally appropriate practices by establishing training and policies promoting breastfeeding.

Md. State Personnel and Pensions Code Ann. § 2-310 (2018) requires the State, through its appropriate officers and employees, to provide a reasonable break time for employees to express breast milk and, on notice, to provide a certain place that may be used by an employee to express breast milk, prohibits the State from being required to compensate an employee receiving reasonable break time for any time spent expressing breast milk at work (HB 306).

Massachusetts

Mass. Gen. Laws Ann. Ch. 111 § 221 (2008) allows a mother to breastfeed her child in any public place or establishment or place which is open to and accepts or solicits the patronage of the general public and where the mother and her child may otherwise lawfully be present. The law also specifies that the act of a mother breastfeeding her child shall not be considered lewd, indecent, immoral or unlawful conduct and provides for a civil action by a mother subjected to a violation of this law.

Mass. Gen. Laws Ann. Ch. 151B § 4 (2018) provides that it is unlawful discrimination for an employer to deny a reasonable accommodation for an employee's pregnancy or any condition related to the employee's pregnancy including, but not limited to, lactation or the need to express breast milk. (HB 3680).

Michigan

Mich. Comp. Laws § 41.181, § 67.1 and § 117.4i (1994) state that public nudity laws do not apply to a woman breastfeeding a child. HB 5313 (2017) specifies public nudity does not include a woman breastfeeding her baby whether or not the nipple or areola is exposed during or incidental to the feeding.

Mich. Comp. Laws § 600.1307a (2012) provides an exemption for nursing mothers from jury service for the period during which she is nursing her child. The mother is exempt upon making the request if she provides a letter from a physician, lactation consultant, or a certified nurse midwife verifying that she is a nursing mother.

Mich. Comp. Laws § 37.231 - § 37.232 (2014) prohibit discriminatory practices, policies, and customs in the exercise of the right to breastfeed and provides for enforcement of the right to breastfeed.

MI HB 5313 (2018) exempts breastfeeding women from public nudity laws.

Minnesota

Minn. Stat. Ann. § 145.894 (1990) directs the state commissioner of health to develop and implement a public education program promoting the provisions of the Maternal and Child Nutrition Act. The education programs must include a campaign to promote breastfeeding.

Minn. Stat. § 145.905 (1998) provides that a mother may breastfeed in any location, public or private, where the mother and child are authorized to be, irrespective of whether the nipple of the mother's breast is uncovered during or incidental to the breastfeeding.

Minn. Stat. § 181.939 (1998) requires employers to provide daily, unpaid break time for a mother to express breast milk for her infant child. HB 2536 (2014) states that employers are also required to make a reasonable effort to provide a private location, other than a bathroom or toilet stall, in close proximity to the workplace that is shielded from view, free from intrusion and has an electrical outlet. The law specifies that an employer may not retaliate against an employee for asserting rights or remedies under this act.

Minn. Stat. Ann. § 617.23 (1998) specifies that breastfeeding does not constitute indecent exposure.

Mississippi

Miss. Code Ann. § 13-5-23 (2006) provides that breastfeeding mothers may be excused from serving as jurors.

Miss. Code Ann. § 17-25-7 - § 17-25-9 (2006) prohibits any ordinance restricting a woman's right to breastfeed and provides that a mother may breastfeed her child in any location she is otherwise authorized to be.

Miss. Code Ann. § 43-20-31 (2006) requires licensed childcare facilities to provide breastfeeding mothers with a sanitary place that is not a toilet stall to breastfeed their children or express milk, to provide a refrigerator to store expressed milk, to train staff in the safe and proper storage and handling of human milk, and to display breastfeeding promotion information to the clients of the facility.

Miss. Code Ann. Ch. 1 § 71-1-55 (2006) prohibits against discrimination towards breastfeeding mothers who use lawful break time to express milk.

Miss. Code Ann. § 97-29-31 and § 97-35-7 (2006) specifies that a woman breastfeeding may not be considered an act of indecent exposure, disorderly conduct, or disturbance of the public space.

Miss. Code Ann. § 43-20-31 (2006) requires licensed childcare facilities to provide a sanitary place that is not a toilet stall that has an electrical outlet, comfortable chair and nearby access to running water for mothers to breastfeed their children.

Miss. Code Ann. § 41-135-7 (2016) states the State Department of Health shall prepare a statement of rights regarding "Breast-Feeding in Mississippi: Guidelines."

Miss. Code Ann. § 41-135-5 (2016) states hospitals that provide birth services may adopt an infant feeding policy that promotes and supports breastfeeding.

Missouri

Mo. Rev. Stat. § 191.915 (1999) requires hospitals and ambulatory surgical centers to provide new mothers with a breastfeeding consultation or information on breastfeeding, the benefits to the child and information on local breastfeeding support groups. The law requires physicians who provide obstetrical or gynecological consultation to inform patients about the postnatal benefits of breastfeeding. The law requires the Department of Health to provide and distribute written information on breastfeeding and the health benefits to the child.

Mo. Rev. Stat. § 191.918 (1999) allows a mother, with discretion, to breastfeed her child in any public or private location where the mother is otherwise authorized to be. HB 1320 (2014) added language stating that the act of a mother breastfeeding or expressing breast milk in a public or private location where the mother and child are otherwise authorized to be shall not constitute sexual conduct or sexual contact as defined in § 566.010, and is not considered an act of public indecency, indecent exposure, lewd touching or obscenity. A municipality may not enact an ordinance prohibiting or restricting a mother from breastfeeding or expressing breast milk in a public or private location.

Mo. Rev. Stat § 494.430 (2014) allows a nursing mother, upon her request, and with a completed written statement from her physician to the court certifying she is a nursing mother, to be excused from service as a petit or grand juror.

Montana

Mont. Code Ann. § 50-19-501 (1999) states that the breastfeeding of a child in any location, public or private, where the mother otherwise has a right to be is legal and cannot be considered a nuisance, indecent exposure, sexual conduct, or obscenity.

Mont. Code Ann. § 39-2-215 et seq. (2007) specifies that employers must not discriminate against breastfeeding mothers and must encourage and accommodate breastfeeding. Requires employers to provide daily unpaid break time for a mother to express breast milk for her infant child, if breaks are currently allowed, and facilities for storage of the expressed milk. Employers are also required to make a reasonable effort to provide a private location, other than a toilet stall, in close proximity to the workplace for this activity.

Mont. Code Ann. § 3-15-313 (2009) specifies that the court may excuse a person from jury service upon finding that it would entail undue hardship for the person; an excuse may be granted if the prospective juror is a breastfeeding mother.

Nebraska

Neb. Rev. Stat. §25-1601-4 (2003) states that a nursing mother is excused from jury duty until she is no longer nursing her child and that she may be required to file a qualification form supported by a certificate from her physician requesting exemption.

Neb. Rev. Stat. § 20-170 (2011) specifies that a mother may breastfeed her child in any public or private location where the mother is otherwise authorized to be. LB 427 (2017) requires schools to have a written policy related to accommodating breastfeeding students in schools with private, and hygienic spaces to express breast milk during the school day.

Nevada

Nev. Rev. Stat. § 201.210, and § 201.220 (1995) state that the breastfeeding of a child is not considered a violation of indecent exposure laws.

Nev. Rev. Stat. § 201.232 (1995) states that a mother may breastfeed her child in any location, private or public, where the mother is otherwise authorized to be.

New Hampshire

N.H. Rev. Stat. Ann. § 132:10-d (1999) state that breastfeeding does not constitute indecent exposure and that limiting or restricting a mother's right to breastfeed is discriminatory.

N.H. Rev. Stat. Ann. § 275-77 (2018) establishes an advisory council on lactation to consider the goals of the United States Surgeon General and the United States Breastfeeding Committee and to examine best practices in the State including specified programs already in place.

New Jersey

N.J. Rev. Stat. § 26:4B-4 (1997) entitles a mother to breastfeed her baby in any location of a place of public accommodation, resort or amusement wherein the mother is otherwise permitted. Failure to comply with the law may result in a fine.

N.J. Rev. Stat. § 10:5-12 (2018) makes it an unlawful employment practice to discriminate based on pregnancy or breastfeeding in compensation or financial terms of employment.

N.J. Rev. Stat §54:32B-1 (2018) exempts breast pumps, breast-pump repair and replacement parts, breast-pump collection and storage supplies and certain breast-pump kits from sales tax.

N.J. Rev. Stat. § 30:4-82.8 (2019) restricts the use of isolated confinement in correctional facilities, prohibits holding an inmate in isolated confinement based on several factors, including pregnant or breastfeeding status.

N.J. Rev. Stat. § 26:4C et. seq. (2019) requires certain public facilities and offices to provide an on-site lactation room, requires the Department of Health to provide information about lactation room availability, requires the Department of Education to provide information on lactation policies in schools.

N.J. Rev. Stat. § 30:4D-6 (2019) requires Medicaid coverage for pasteurized donated human breast milk, under certain circumstances.

N.J. Rev. Stat. § 30:4D-6o (2019) requires health benefits and Medicaid coverage for breastfeeding support.

N.J. Rev. Stat. § 9:6-8.98.1 (2019) requires the Child Fatality and Near Fatality Review Board to study racial and ethnic disparities that contribute to infant mortality, addresses disparities in breastfeeding initiation and duration to increase supports among racial and ethnic populations.

New Mexico

N.M. Stat. Ann. § 28-20-1 (1999) permits a mother to breastfeed her child in any public or private location where she is otherwise authorized to be.

N.M. Stat. Ann. § 28-20-2 (2007) requires employers to provide a clean, private place, not a bathroom, for employees who are breastfeeding to pump. Also requires that the employee be given breaks to express milk, but does not require that she be paid for this time.

NM SB 124 (2019) provides that correctional facilities housing female inmates develop and implement a breastfeeding and lactation policy based on current, accepted best practices.

NM SB 192 (2019) requires courts to consider pregnancy or lactation for release, bond or good time computation.

New York

N.Y. Public Health Law § 2505 (1980) provides that the Maternal and Child Health commissioner has the power to adopt regulations and guidelines including, but not limited to donor standards, methods of collection, and standards for storage and distribution of human breast milk.

N.Y. Penal Law § 245.01 et seq. (1984) excludes breastfeeding of infants from exposure offenses.

N.Y. Civil Rights Law § 79-E (1994) permits a mother to breastfeed her child in any public or private location.

N.Y. Labor Law § 206-C (2007) states that employers must allow breastfeeding mothers reasonable, unpaid break times to express milk and make a reasonable attempt to provide a private location for her to do so. Prohibits discrimination against breastfeeding mothers.

N.Y. Correction Law § 611 (2009) allows a mother of a nursing child to be accompanied by her child if she is committed to a correctional facility at the time she is breastfeeding. This law also permits a child born to a committed mother to return with the mother to the correctional facility. The child may remain with the mother until one year of age if the woman is physically capable of caring for the child.

N.Y. Public Health Law § 2505-A (2009) creates the Breastfeeding Mothers Bill of Rights and requires it to be posted in a public place in each maternal health care facility. The commissioner must also make the Breastfeeding Mothers Bill of Rights available on the health department's website so that health care facilities and providers may include such rights in a maternity information leaflet.

NY SB 2007 (2018) includes pasteurized donor human milk, which may include fortifiers as medically indicated for inpatient use, under standard coverage for medical assistance for needy persons under certain conditions.

NY AB 9508 (2018) requires that a covered public building shall contain a lactation room that is made available for use by a member of the public to breastfeed or express breast milk.

NY AB 748 (2019) amends the Judiciary Law, provides an exemption from jury duty for breastfeeding women, allows that such breastfeeding mother's jury duty shall be postponed up to a certain period after the date on which such service otherwise to commence.

North Carolina

N.C. Gen. Stat. § 14-190.9 (1993) states that a woman is allowed to breastfeed in any public or private location, and that she is not in violation of indecent exposure laws.

North Dakota

N.D. Cent. Code § 12.1-20-12.1 (2009) exempts the act of a woman discreetly breastfeeding her child from indecent exposure laws.

N.D. Cent. Code § 23-12-16 (2009) allows a woman to breastfeed her child in any location, public or private, where the woman and child are otherwise authorized to be.

N.D. Cent. Code § 23-12-17 (2009) provides that an employer may use the designation "infant friendly" on its promotional materials if the employer adopts specified workplace breastfeeding policies, including scheduling breaks and permitting work patterns that provide time for expression of breast milk; providing a convenient, sanitary, safe and private location other than a restroom for expressing breast milk; and a refrigerator in the workplace for the temporary storage of breast milk. The law also directs to the state department of health to establish guidelines for employers concerning workplace breastfeeding and infant friendly designations.

Ohio

Ohio Rev. Code Ann. § 3781.55 (2005) provides that a mother is entitled to breastfeed her baby in any location of a place of public accommodation wherein the mother is otherwise permitted.

Oklahoma

Okla. Stat. tit. 38, § 28 (2004) exempts mothers who are breastfeeding a baby from jury duty, upon their request.

Okla. Stat. tit. 63, § 1-234 (2004) allow a mother to breastfeed her child in any location that she is authorized to be and exempts her from the crimes and punishments listed in the penal code of the state of Oklahoma.

Okla. Stat. tit. 40, § 435 (2006) requires that an employer provide reasonable unpaid break time each day to an employee who needs to breastfeed or express breast milk for her child. The law requires the Department of Health to issue periodic reports on breastfeeding rates, complaints received, and benefits reported by both working breastfeeding mothers and employers.

OK SB 285 (2020) relates to the accommodation for expressing milk and breast feeding; requires state agencies to allow paid break times for lactating employees to a use lactation room for certain purposes.

OK SB 1877 (2020) relates to public buildings; requires appropriate authority of a covered public building to ensure availability of a lactation room.

Oregon

Or. Rev. Stat. § 10.050 (1999) excuses a woman from acting as a juror if the woman is breastfeeding a child. A request from the woman must be made in writing.

Or. Rev. Stat. § 109.001 (1999) allows a woman to breastfeed in a public place.

Or. Rev. Stat. § 653.075, § 653.077 and § 653.256 (2007) allow women to have unpaid 30-minute breaks during each four-hour shift to breastfeed or pump. Allows certain exemptions for employers.

OR HB 2005 (2019) creates the Family and Medical Leave Insurance Program. Provides that benefits may be extended for an additional two weeks for covered individuals experiencing conditions related to pregnancy, including but not limited to lactation.

OR HB 2341 (2019) makes unlawful employment practice for employer to deny reasonable accommodation to known limitations related to pregnancy, childbirth or related medical condition, including lactation.

OR HB 2593 (2019) conforms state law related to expression of milk in the workplace to federal law, eliminates the exemption from providing rest periods for expression of milk in the workplace if granting rest period imposes undue hardship.

Pennsylvania

Act No. 28 of 2007 allows mothers to breastfeed in public without penalty. Breastfeeding may not be considered a nuisance, obscenity or indecent exposure under this law.

Pa. Cons. Stat. tit. 42 § 4503 (2015) allows breastfeeding women who request to be excused, to be exempt or excused from jury duty.

Act. No. 7 of 2020 enacts the Keystone Mothers' Milk Bank Act; revises provisions regulating milk banks that provide donor human milk in this Commonwealth; expands licensee requirements; provides for the inspection of facilities and documentation; provides certain exemptions.

Puerto Rico

1 L.P.R.A. § 5165 (2003) declares August as "Breastfeeding Awareness Month" and the first week of August as "World Breastfeeding Week" in Puerto Rico.

34 L.P.R.A. § 1735h (2003) states that any woman breastfeeding her child under 24 months old and who presents a medical attestation to such fact is exempt from serving as a juror.

24 L.P.R.A. § 3518 (2004) states that a mother breastfeeding her child in any place, whether public or private, where she is otherwise authorized to be, shall not be deemed as indecent exposure, obscene act or other punishable action.

3 L.P.R.A. § 1466 and 29 L.P.R.A. § 478a et seq. provide that breastfeeding mothers have the opportunity to breastfeed their babies for half an hour within the full-time working day for a maximum duration of 12 months.

23 L.P.R.A. § 43-1 directs the Regulations and Permits Administration to adopt regulations, which shall provide that in shopping malls, airports, ports and public service government centers there shall be accessible areas designed for breastfeeding and diaper changing that are not bathrooms.

Rhode Island

R.I. Gen. Laws § 11-45-2 (1998) specifies that indecent exposure-disorderly conduct laws do not apply to breastfeeding in public.

R.I. Gen. Laws § 23-13.2-1 (2003) specifies that an employer may provide reasonable unpaid break time each day to an employee who needs to breastfeed or express breast milk for her infant child. The law requires the department of health to issue periodic reports on breastfeeding rates, complaints received, and benefits reported by both working breastfeeding mothers and employers, and provides definitions.

R.I. Gen. Laws § 23-13.5-1 and § 23-13.5-2 (2008) allow a woman to feed her child by bottle or breast in any place open to the public and would allow her a private cause of action for denial of this right.

South Carolina

S.C. Code Ann. § 63-5-40 (2008) provides that a woman may breastfeed her child in any location where the mother is authorized to be and that the act of breastfeeding is not considered indecent exposure.

S.C. Code Ann. § 1-13-80 (2018) enacts the Pregnancy Accommodations Act, relates to definitions under the human affairs laws, revises the terms because of sex or on the basis of sex used in the context of equal treatment for women affected by pregnancy, childbirth or related medical conditions, relates to unlawful employment practices of an employer and lactation, provides for certain other unlawful employment practices in regard to failure to provide reasonable accommodations for an applicant for employment or employee (HB 3865).

SC HB 3200 (2020) enacts the Lactation Support Act; provides that employers shall provide employees with reasonable unpaid break time daily or shall permit employees to use paid break time or mealtime to express breast milk; provides that employers shall make reasonable efforts to provide certain areas where employees may express breast milk; provides that employers may not discriminate against employees for choosing to express breast milk in the workplace.

South Dakota

S.D. Codified Laws Ann. § 22-24A-2 (2002) exempts mothers who are breastfeeding from indecency laws.

S.D. Codified Laws Ann. § 16-13-10.4 (2012) provides for an exemption from jury duty for a mother who is breastfeeding a baby younger than one year. A written notice requesting an exemption must be submitted to the clerk of court within ten days of receiving the summons for jury duty.

Tennessee

Tenn. Code Ann. § 50-1-305 (1999) requires employers to provide daily unpaid break time for a mother to express breast milk for her infant child. Employers are also required to make a reasonable effort to provide a private location, other than a toilet stall, in close proximity to the workplace for this activity.

Tenn. Code Ann. § 68-58-101 et seq. (2006) permit a mother to breastfeed in any location, public or private, that the mother is authorized to be, and prohibits local governments from criminalizing or restricting breastfeeding. Specifies that the act of breastfeeding shall not be considered public indecency or nudity, obscene, or sexual conduct. SB 83 (2011) removed the age limitation in statute permitting mothers to publicly breastfeed only their children who are age 12 months or younger.

TN SB 2520 (2020) enacts the Pregnant Workers Fairness Act; sets forth fair employment practices and protections for pregnant workers.

Texas

Tex. Health Code Ann. § 165.002 (1995) authorizes a woman to breastfeed her child in any location.

Tex. Health Code Ann. § 165.003 (1995) provides for the use of a "mother-friendly" designation for businesses who have policies supporting worksite breastfeeding.

Tex. Health Code Ann. § 165.032 (1995) provides for a worksite breastfeeding demonstration project and requires the Department of Health to develop recommendations supporting worksite breastfeeding.

Tex. Health Code Ann. § 161.071 (2001) requires the Department of Health to establish minimum guidelines for the procurement, processing, distribution, or use of human milk by donor milk banks.

TX HB 475 (2019) includes infant nutrition and the importance of breastfeeding in a list of information to be disseminated to foster children that are pregnant and minors who are pregnant by the Department of Health.

TX HB 541 (2019) relates to the right to express breast milk, provides that a mother is entitled to breastfeed her baby or express breast milk in any location in which the mother's presence is otherwise authorized to be.

U.S. Virgin Islands

14 V.I.C. § 1022 (2002) specifies that a woman breastfeeding a child in any public or private location where the woman's presence is otherwise authorized does not under any circumstance constitute obscene or indecent conduct.

Utah

Utah Code Ann. § 17-15-25 (1995) states that the county legislative body may not prohibit a woman's breastfeeding in any location where she otherwise may rightfully be, regardless of whether the breast is uncovered during or incidental to the breastfeeding.

Utah Code Ann. § 76-9-702 and § 76-10-1229.5 (1995) state that a breastfeeding woman is not in violation of any lewdness, obscene or indecent exposure laws.

Utah HJR 4 (2012) encourages employers to recognize the benefits of breastfeeding and to provide unpaid break time and an appropriate space for employees who need to breastfeed or express their milk for their infant children.

Utah Code Ann. § 34-49-101 et. seq. (2015) requires a public employer to provide reasonable breaks for a mother who needs to express breast milk and a room or other location in close proximity to the employee's work area that is not a bathroom, is private, and has an electrical outlet. The employer shall also provide access to a clean refrigerator or freezer for the storage of breast milk.

Utah Code Ann. § 78B-1-109 (2015) states that a court may excuse an individual from jury service upon showing the individual is a mother who is breastfeeding a child. The individual must make the showing by affidavit, sworn testimony, or other competent evidence.

Utah Code Ann. § 34A-5-106 (2016) states that it is a discriminatory and prohibited practice for an employer to refuse to provide reasonable accommodations for an employee related to pregnancy, childbirth, breastfeeding or related conditions if the employee requests it and unless the employer demonstrates the accommodation would create an undue hardship. An employer also may not require an employee to terminate employment or deny employment opportunities based on the need for an employer to make reasonable accommodations.

UT HB 196 (2018) creates the Breastfeeding Protection Act, amends provisions related to public accommodations, prohibits discrimination based on pregnancy in places of public accommodation, permits a woman to breastfeed in any place of public accommodation.

Vermont

Vt. Stat. Ann. tit. 9, § 4502 (j) (2002) provides that a mother may breastfeed her child in any place of public accommodation in which the mother and child would otherwise have a legal right to be.

Vt. Stat. Ann. tit. 21, § 305 (2008) requires employers to provide reasonable time throughout the day for nursing mothers to express breast milk for three years after the birth of a child. Also requires employers to make a reasonable accommodation to provide appropriate private space that is not a bathroom stall, and prohibits discrimination against an employee who exercises or attempts to exercise the rights provided under this act.

Vt. Acts, Act 203 (2008) directs the commissioner of health to convene a healthy worksites work group to identify priorities and develop recommendations to enhance collaborative learning and interactive sharing of best practices in worksite wellness and employee health management. The work group shall examine best practices in Vermont and other states, including strategies to spread the adoption of workplace policies and practices that support breastfeeding for mothers.

Virginia

Va. Code Ann. § 18.2-387 (1994) exempts mothers engaged in breastfeeding from indecent exposure laws.

Va. HJR 145 (2002) encourages employers to recognize the benefits of breastfeeding and to provide unpaid break time and appropriate space for employees to breastfeed or express milk.

Va. Code § 2.2-3903 (2002) states that no employer with more than five but less than 15 employees shall discharge an employee on the basis of certain factors, including pregnancy, childbirth or related medical conditions, including lactation.

Va. Code § 2.2-1147.1 (2002) and § 32.1-370 (2015) guarantee a woman the right to breastfeed her child on in any place where the mother is lawfully present, including any location where she would otherwise be allowed on property that is owned, leased or controlled by the state.

Va. Code Ann. § 8.01-341.1 (2005) provides that a mother who is breastfeeding a child may be exempted from jury duty upon her request.

Va. Code § 22.1-79.6 (2014) Directs each local school board to adopt a policy to set aside, in each school in the school division, a non-restroom location that is shielded from the public view to be designated as an area in which any mother who is employed by the local school board or enrolled as a student may take breaks of reasonable length during the school day to express milk to feed her child until the child reaches the age of one.

VA SJR 298 (2019) designates August, in 2019 and in each succeeding year, as Breastfeeding Awareness Month in Virginia.

Va. Code Ann. § 2.2-1201 (2019) directs the Department of Human Resource Management to develop state personnel policies that provide break time for nursing mothers to express breast milk.

VA HB 827 (2020) relates to the Virginia Human Rights Act; prohibits discrimination on the basis of pregnancy, childbirth, or related medical conditions, including lactation; requires employers to make reasonable accommodation for the known limitations of a person related to pregnancy, childbirth, or related medical conditions, including lactation, if such accommodation is necessary; sets forth prohibited actions by employers; provides for actions against employers in violation of the Act.

VA SB 868 (2020) relates to prohibited discrimination on the basis of several factors, including lactation; relates to public accommodations, employment, credit, and housing; creates explicit causes of action for unlawful discrimination in public accommodations and employment in the Human Rights Act.

Washington

Wash. Rev. Code § 9A.88.010 (2001) states that the act of breastfeeding or expressing breast milk is not indecent exposure.

Wash. Rev. Code § 43.70.640 (2001) allows any employer, governmental and private, to use the designation of "infant-friendly" on its promotional materials if the employer has an approved workplace breastfeeding policy with certain requirements, including flexible work scheduling with breaks to express breast milk and a location other than a restroom for breastfeeding.

Wash. Rev. Code § 49.60.30(g) and § 49.60.215 (2009) provides that it is the right of a mother to breastfeed her child in any place of public resort, accommodations, assemblage or amusement and that it is an unfair practice for any person to discriminate against a mother breastfeeding her child in any such place.

Wash. Rev. Code § 74.09.475 (2017) requires all health care facilities that provide newborn delivery services to medical assistance clients to establish a strategy to promote maternal and child health outcomes, including elements to promote breastfeeding.

Wash. Rev. Code § 72.09.588 (2018) requires incarcerated women have access to midwifery or doula services, including breastfeeding assistance (HB 2016).

Wash. Rev. Code 43.10.005 (2019) revises provisions related to the expression of breast milk in the workplace, expands the definition of reasonable accommodation to provide reasonable break times for an employee to express breast milk for a certain number of years after a child's birth and to provide a private location, other than a bathroom, for such purpose. (HB 1930)

West Virginia

W. Va Code § 61-8-9 (2007) states that it is not considered indecent exposure for a mother to breastfeed in any location, public or private.

W. Va Code § 16-1-19 (2014) provides that a mother may breastfeed a child in any location open to the public.

WV SB 1037 (2019) requires a safety insert for medical cannabis to include a warning to pregnant and breastfeeding women about the risks of using cannabis while pregnant or breastfeeding.

Wisconsin

Wis. Stat. § 944.17(3), § 944.20(2) and § 948.10(2)(b) (1995) provide that breastfeeding mothers are not in violation of criminal statutes of indecent or obscene exposure.

Wis. Stat. § 253.165 (2009) provides that a mother may breastfeed her child in any public or private location where the mother and child are otherwise authorized to be. The law specifies that in such a location, no person may prohibit a mother from breastfeeding her child, direct a mother to move to a different location to breastfeed her child, direct a mother to cover her child or breast while breastfeeding, or otherwise restrict a mother from breastfeeding her child.

Wyoming

Wyo. HJR 5 (2003) encourages breastfeeding and recognizes the importance of breastfeeding to maternal and child health. The resolution also commends employers, both in the public and private sectors, who provide accommodations for breastfeeding mothers.

Wyo. Stat. § 6-4-201 (2007) exempts breastfeeding mothers from public indecency laws and gives breastfeeding women the right to nurse anyplace that they otherwise have a right to be.

Appendix 3: A Special Note to Incarcerated Mothers

The following position statement excerpt is shared with permission from the National Commission on Correctional Health Care Board of Directors website. This statement does not guarantee that a woman will be able to breastfeed in correctional settings, however it provides a strong recommendation for administrators of correctional facilities to adopt a policy allowing breastfeeding and guidance on what should be included.

POSITION STATEMENT

"Wherever possible and not precluded by security concerns, correctional facilities that house pregnant and postpartum women should devise systems to enable postpartum women to express breast milk for their babies and to breastfeed them directly.

The following practices are ways to support this objective:

1. Screen women on entry to determine if they are postpartum and breastfeeding.

2. Counsel pregnant women on the benefits and nutritional needs of breastfeeding and inform them of the systems and supports in place at the facility.

3. Provide breastfeeding women with a special diet with appropriate caloric, fluid, calcium, and vitamin D intake. Prenatal vitamins offer a convenient way to provide essential nutrients that are often missing from correctional diets.

4. Allow immediately postpartum women to breastfeed their babies and have lactation support services from the hospital.

5. Support visiting arrangements that allow direct contact between infants and mothers.

6. Provide accommodations to express breast milk, since regular breastfeeding on infant demand is rarely feasible for women in custody. Accommodations may include providing a manual or electric breast pump and storage bags, a private place to pump on a frequent basis, a freezer, and a system for proper storage of the breast milk and, when possible, transfer to the infant.

7. Establish nursery programs or alternative programs for postpartum women that will allow the infants to stay with their mothers, making breastfeeding much easier.

8. Develop an arrangement for lactation specialist services to provide support to women who need it."

Appendix 4. Breastfeeding Support Organizations, Birthing & Post-Partum Resources and More

NATIONAL ORGANIZATIONS

Webbmark Health Solutions
Memphis, TN
731-215-0385
larita@webbmarkhealth.com

La Leche League International
110 Horizon Drive, Suite 210
Raleigh, NC 27615
Main: +1 919.459.2167
Direct: +1 919.459.8584
Fax: +1 919.459.2075
Web: www.llli.org

National Database of Lactation Support Groups for Families of Color

bit.ly/natsupgrp

Black Mothers Breastfeeding Association
Detroit, MI
www.BMBFA.org
info@BMBFA.org
(800)313-6141
Twitter, Facebook, Instagram: @BMBFA

BREASTFEEDING SUPPORT GROUPS BY STATE

Florida

Lioness Lactation LLC
www.LionessLactation.com

Georgia

Reaching Our Sisters Everywhere (ROSE)
Reaching Our Sisters Everywhere Inc.
3035 Stone Mountain St. #1076
Lithonia, GA 30058
http://www.breastfeedingrose.org/
Telephone & Fax:
(404) 719-4297

Michigan

Black Mothers Breastfeeding Association
Detroit, MI
www.BMBFA.org
info@BMBFA.org
(800)313-6141
Twitter, Facebook, Instagram: @BMBFA

Southeast Michigan IBCLCs of Color (SEMI)
semichioc@gmail.com
www.semiibclcofcolor.org
https://www.facebook.com/SMIBCLCsofColor
https://www.instagram.com/semi_ibclc.oc/

Mississippi

The Lactating Club (TLC) Baby Café
crossroadsbabycafe@gmail.com
Chelesa Presley
P.O. Box 252
Clarksdale, MS 38614
Facebook/TLCbabycafe
IG The Lactating Club

Pennsylvania

BAE Cafe
BAE Culture, LLC
baeculture.org
Philadelphia, PA

Life House Lactation & Perinatal Services
www.thelactationtherapist.com

Tennessee

Webbmark Health Solutions
Memphis, TN
731-215-0385
larita@webbmarkhealth.com

Breastfeeding Sistas that are Receiving Support
(BSTARS)
PO Box 141053
Memphis, TN 38114
Attn: Tiana Pyles
info@bstars.org
@BSTARS901

Meharry Medical College
Breastfeeding Promotion Program
Nashville, TN
615-327-5653
fukoli@mmc.edu

TN Breastfeeding Hotline (24 Hours)
1-855- BF4MOMS
1-855-423-6667

BREASTMILK DONATION CENTERS

Human Milk Bank Association of North America
www.hmbana.org

BIRTHING AND POST-PARTUM SUPPORT ORGANIZATIONS

CHOICES Memphis Center for Reproductive Health
1203 Poplar Avenue
Memphis, TN 38104
901-274-3550

Midwives

Nikia Grayson, DNP, MPH, CNM, FNP-C
Director of Clinical Services/Family Nurse Midwife
1203 Poplar Avenue
Memphis, TN 38104
901-274-3550 ex 232
ngrayson@memphischoices.org

Doulas

Perinatal Health Services/Doulawithak
Kimathi D Street Coleman, CLC
Memphis, TN
901-310-5372
creationswithak@gmail.com

Refuge Birth Doula
Sjhira Ellzey
Nashville, TN
Refugebirthdoula@gmail.com
www.refugebirth.com

**PRESCRIPTON DRUG & SUPPLEMENTS
INTERACTIONS WITH BREASTMILK
DATABASE**

LactMed by the National Center for Biotechnology
Information
https://www.ncbi.nlm.nih.gov/books/NBK501922/

This is a database that contains an extensive list of
pharmaceutical drugs and supplements and documents
any known effects of the drug or supplement on
breastmilk. If you are taking any prescription or over
the counter drugs or supplements, please check the
database to ensure it is safe to use during breastfeeding,
but always consult your medical provider.

LEGAL ADVOCACY ORGANIZATIONS

Center for Work Life Law
Free legal helpline: 415-703-8276
Email: hotline@worklifelaw.org.
Workers' website:
https://www.pregnantatwork.org/pregnant-women-pregnancy/breastfeeding-employees/

Students' website:
https://thepregnantscholar.org/know-your-rights-breastfeeding/

National Commission on Correctional Health Care
1145 W. Diversey Pkwy.
Chicago, IL 60614
P | 773-880-1460
F | 773-880-2424
Email | info@ncchc.org
www.ncchc.org

RESEARCH

Academy of Breastfeeding Medicine
https://www.bfmed.org/
They publish scholarly research articles about the latest evidence regarding breastfeeding.

American Pediatric Association
www.healthychildren.org

About the Author

Dr. Larita Taylor is not another "talking head", but an enthusiastic health coach. Before she became a mother, she was already a breastfeeding advocate conducting public health research designed to reduce racial disparities in breastfeeding and birth outcomes through her company Webbmark Health Solutions. The struggles she overcame to breastfeed her two children only amplified her advocacy efforts and led her to become a certified lactation counselor. As an alumnus of Fuller Theological Seminary and a former director of congregational care for a megachurch, she is well acquainted with caring for the spiritual, physical, and emotional needs of others while maintaining self-care practices. She is a proud Vanderbilt Commodore and two-time graduate of the University of Memphis School of Public Health where she completed her Master's and Doctorate. She resides in TN with her loving husband and joyous children.